D1649747

Maths:
Word Problems

The 11+
10-Minute Tests

For the CEM (Durham University) test

Book 1

Ages
10-11

Practise • Prepare • Pass
Everything your child needs for 11+ success

How to use this book

This book is made up of 10-minute tests and puzzle pages.
There are answers and detailed explanations in the pull-out section at the back of the book.

10-Minute Tests

- There are 31 tests in this book, each containing 12 questions.

- Each test is designed to target the type of context-based maths questions that your child could come across in their 11+ test, and covers a variety of topics at the right difficulty levels.

- Your child should aim to score around 10 or 11 out of 12 in each 10-minute test.
  If they score less than this, use their results to work out the areas they need more practice on.

- If your child hasn't managed to finish the test in time, they need to work on increasing their speed, whereas if they have made a lot of mistakes, they need to work more carefully.

- Keep track of your child's scores using the progress chart on the inside back cover of the book.

Puzzle Pages

- There are 12 puzzle pages in this book, which are a great break from test-style questions.
  They encourage children to practise similar skills that they will need in the test, but in a fun way.

Published by CGP

Editors:
David Maliphant, Andy Park, Ben Train

With thanks to Alison Griffin and Paul Jordin for the proofreading.

Please note that CGP is not associated with CEM or The University of Durham in any way.
This book does not include any official questions and it is not endorsed by CEM or The University of Durham.
CEM, Centre for Evaluation and Monitoring, Durham University and *The University of Durham*
are all trademarks of The University of Durham.

ISBN: 978 1 78294 600 7
Printed by Elanders Ltd, Newcastle upon Tyne
Clipart from Corel®

Based on the classic CGP style created by Richard Parsons.

Text, design, layout and original illustrations © Coordination Group Publications Ltd. (CGP) 2015
All rights reserved.

Photocopying this book is not permitted. Extra copies are available from CGP with next day delivery.
0800 1712 712 • www.cgpbooks.co.uk

Contents

Test 3 was done long time ago

You have **10 minutes** to do this test. Work as quickly and accurately as you can.

1. Four friends share £1044 equally.
   How much does each friend get?

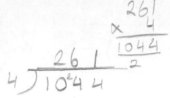

£ 2 6 1 0 0

2. There are five people in a group and they each own the same number of marbles.
   Circle the option below that could show the total number of marbles they own.

   A 458   **C** 376   **E** 412

   B 951   **D** 295   ✗

3. Rob's score on a new video game is shown below.

   SCORE: **346 581**

   What is the value of the 6 in his score? Circle the correct option below.

   A 6   **C** 6000   **E** 60 000

   B 60   **D** 600   ✓

4. The pie below is being eaten by five people. The angle of each slice is shown.

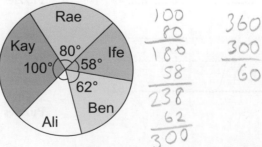

   What is the angle of Ali's slice?

   6 0 °   ✓

5. In a bag of tropical fruit mix, $^{18}/_{25}$ is made up of carbohydrates.
    What is this as a percentage?

    $\frac{18}{25_1} \times \overset{4}{\cancel{100}} = 72$ $\begin{array}{r} \overset{1}{18} \\ \times\,4 \\ \hline 72 \\ \hline 3 \end{array}$ $\boxed{7}\,\boxed{2}$ %

The chart below shows the expected daily rainfall (in mm) in July
for several UK holiday destinations.

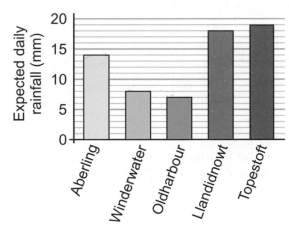

6. How much more rain is expected to fall each day in Topestoft than in Oldharbour?
    Give your answer in centimetres.

    $\boxed{}.\boxed{1}.\boxed{2}$ cm ✓

7. How much more rain is expected to fall in Aberling than in Winderwater
    during the whole month of July?

    $\boxed{}\boxed{6}\boxed{0}\boxed{0}$ mm

    ✗

8. Sammy is facing West. He turns 225° in an anticlockwise direction.
    Which direction is he now facing? Circle the correct answer.

    A   North East
    B   South West
    C   East
    (D) South East
    E   North West

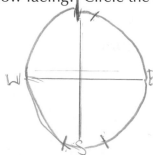

9. It takes Haruko 3³/₄ hours to cycle to his uncle's house.
How many minutes is this?

3 h ─D180m (60x3)   180
                     45
¾ of 60 = 45 m   225

[2][2][5] minutes ✓

10. Bina ate ¹/₄ of a pizza. Sean ate twice as much of the pizza as Bina.
Rebeka then had half as much of the pizza as Bina.
What fraction of the pizza is left? Circle the correct answer.

A   ¹/₁₆   Ⓒ   ³/₈   E   ¹/₈
B   ¹/₄   D   ⁷/₈

✗

11. Three corners of a square have coordinates (3, 2), (1, 5) and (4, 7).
Some treasure is buried at the fourth corner
of the square. Where is the treasure buried?
Circle the correct answer.

A   (7, 5)
B   (2, 6)
C   (6, 2)
Ⓓ   (6, 4)   ✓
E   (4, 6)

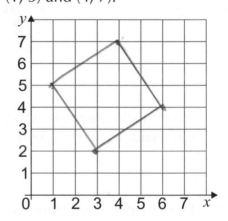

12. The number of bugs living in a colony increases each day.
To find the number of bugs in the colony each day, multiply
the number of bugs on the previous day by 2, and then add 1.
Circle the number that cannot show a possible number of bugs
in the colony after 10 days.

A   12 286   C   9215   Ⓔ   16 383
B   6143   D   3071

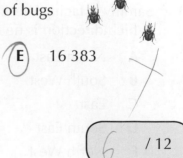

✗

6 / 12

You have **10 minutes** to do this test. Work as quickly and accurately as you can.

1. Richard takes a trip across America. On his journey the coldest temperature he records is –32 °C. The hottest temperature he records is 41°C.
    What is the difference between these two temperatures?

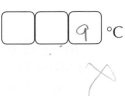

°C

Asuka's garden is in the shape of a parallelogram, as shown.

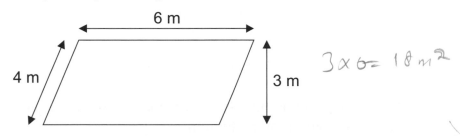

$3 \times 6 = 18 m^2$

2. What is the perimeter of Asuka's garden?

m

3. What is the area of the garden? Circle the correct option.

    A   20 m²   **C**   18 m²   **E**   9 m²
    B   24 m²   **D**   8 m² $l \times h$

4. The total time for a swimming relay team is found by adding together the times of its four individual swimmers.
    The four swimmers in a team take 38 seconds, 46 seconds, 52 seconds and 50 seconds. What was the team's total time?

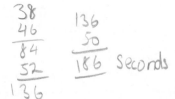

136
50
186 Seconds

3 minutes 0 6 seconds

5. Ben cycles 39.48 miles.
   If 5 miles = 8 kilometres, what is the approximate distance in kilometres that Ben cycled? Circle the correct option below.

   A   25 km   **C**   56 km   **E**   64 km

   B   72 km   **D**   40 km

6. Una goes to the bank for a loan.
   It takes 31 days to approve and then another 3 weeks till the loan is paid.
   What is the total time needed to approve and pay the loan?
   Give your answer in weeks and days.

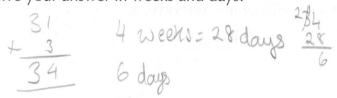

   [ ] [4] weeks [6] days

All the students in a school picked their favourite computer game.
The results are shown in this pictogram.

Game	Number of students	
Shoot Bang Shoot	☺ ☺ ☺	11
Fly Fly Fly	☺ ☺ ☺ ☺ ☺ ◁	21
Wizards and Demons	☺ ☺ ☺ ◁	14
Game of Films	☺ ☺ ◁	10

☺ = 4 students

11
21
14
10
56

7. How many students are in the school altogether? Circle the correct option.

   A   28   **C**   56   **E**   42

   B   7   **D**   14

8. A third of the students who chose Fly Fly Fly as their favourite game are boys.
   How many boys chose Fly Fly Fly as their favourite game?

   [ ] [7]

9. Nicolao knows the next train to Neartown leaves at 9:37 pm.
It arrives in Neartown 1 hour and 28 minutes later.
What time does the train arrive? Give your answer in 24-hour clock format.

$$\begin{array}{r} 9:37 \\ 1:28 \\ \hline 8:09 \end{array}$$

```
 8 : 0 9
```

10. Adjo has a certain amount of time to finish a test, which is made up of 3 parts.
Adjo has taken $\frac{1}{3}$ of the total time to do Part 1,
and $\frac{1}{4}$ of the total time to do Part 2.
What fraction of the total time does he have left for Part 3?
Circle the correct answer.

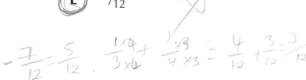

   A $\frac{5}{6}$ **C** $\frac{5}{12}$ **(E)** $\frac{7}{12}$

   B $\frac{3}{12}$ **D** $\frac{5}{24}$

11. Michael builds the object below out of toy cubes with sides of length 3 cm.

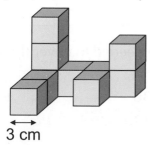

3 cm

What is the volume of the object?

```
      1 2  cm³
```

12. A shop sells picture frames in different sizes. The height (h) and width (w) of each
frame are linked by the formula $h = 1.5w + 12$.
What is the width of a frame that is 27 cm high?

```
    9  cm
```

4 / 12

You have **10 minutes** to do this test. Work as quickly and accurately as you can.

1. Caroline pours 35 millilitres of fruit squash into a glass and adds 0.5 litres of water.
    What is the total volume of her fruit squash drink? Circle the correct answer.

    A   0.535 litres   **C**   535 litres   **E**   850 millilitres
    B   0.85 litres   **D**   0.535 millilitres

2. It takes 2 boxes of tiles to cover an area of 1 m².

    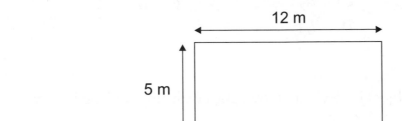

    How many boxes of tiles would be needed to cover the wall above?
    Circle the correct answer.

    A   60   **C**   30   **E**   100
    B   34   **D**   120

3. An antiques dealer buys two clocks on the same day from the same shop.
    She paid £34.50 for one clock and £51 for the other.
    How much change did she receive from £100?

    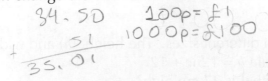

    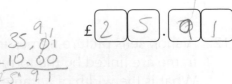

     £2 5 . 9 1

4. A recipe uses 240 g of flour to make a cake for 6 people.
    How much flour would be needed to make a cake for 10 people?
    Circle the correct answer below.

    A   40 g   **C**   360 g   **E**   120 g
    B   4 kg   **D**   400 g

5. A DVD is for sale at different prices in five different stores.
    The prices are £10, £11, £13, £10 and £11.50.
    What is the mean price?

    £ [ ] [2] . [3] [8]

    10
    +11
    13
    33 + 11.

    33
    +10
    43

    11, 50
    43
    11, 93

    2.38
    5)11.9⁴3

    ✗

6. Sam has 60 coloured pencils. The fraction of Sam's pencils that are red is ⁷/₁₂.
    How many of Sam's pencils are not red?

    [ ] [3] [5]

    ✗.

The timetable for a train service between Newcastle and London is shown below.

Newcastle	07:14	10:22	14:38	17:52
York	09:25	12:33	16:49	20:03
Doncaster	10:23	13:31	17:47	21:01
Peterborough	12:31	15:39	19:55	23:13
London	14:09	17:17	21:33	00:51

7. How long does it take the train leaving Newcastle at 10:22 to get to London?

    16 ̶1̶7̶:̶1̶7̶
    -12:22
    6:55

    [0] [6] hours [5] [5] minutes ✓

8. Alf needs to travel from York to Peterborough and must arrive before 7:30 pm.
    It takes him 42 minutes to walk from his house to York station.
    If Alf wants to leave his house as late as possible, when should he set off?
    Circle the correct option.

    A   11:51 am   C   8:43 am   E   6:07 pm   ✗
    B   8:21 pm   (D)   4:07 pm   16:49
                                                     - 42
                                                      16:07

© CGP — not to be photocopied   9

9. A gardener converts temperatures between degrees Celsius (c) and degrees Fahrenheit (f) using the following approximation: $f = 2c + 30$. The temperature today is 18 °C. Find the approximate temperature in °F.

$2c + 30$

$30 - 2c = 28c$

$28c - 18c = 10f$

 °F

✗

10. A farmer piles his containers of winter cow food in triangular stacks.
The stacks form a pattern of triangles which increase in size.
The first three stacks the farmer makes are shown below.

1st stack   2nd stack   3rd stack
(1 container)   (3 containers)   (6 containers)

How many containers will be in the 8th stack?

✗

64

11. The net of a cube is drawn on the piece of card shown below.

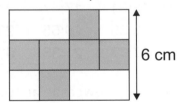

6 cm

What is the volume of the cube?

don't know ✗

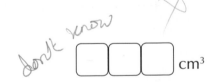 cm³

12. Paul has forgotten his aunt's house number, but he knows:
- it has 2 digits
- it starts with 9
- it is a prime number
What is his aunt's house number?

91

/ 12

© CGP — not to be photocopied

Puzzles 1

Time for a break! These puzzles are a great way to practise your maths skills.

A Night on the Tiles

One evening Sam and Anya are playing a game involving letter tiles.

- Each letter is worth a different whole number of points.
- The score for a word is the sum of the scores for the letters in that word.
- The scores on the tiles are hidden, but Sam has an old scoresheet showing the scores for a few different words.
- Use the scoresheet to find the value of each letter. Then find the scores for the following words.

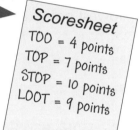

Scoresheet

TOO = 4 points
TOP = 7 points
STOP = 10 points
LOOT = 9 points

a) **P O S T**

b) **P L O T S**

c) **S P O O L S**

Breaking Up is Hard To Do

- I've got a chocolate bar made up of 20 individual chunks, as shown on the right. I want to break it into 20 separate chunks.

- I can break a maximum of two 'stacked' pieces of chocolate at the same time.

 ✓    ✗

- What's the smallest number of separate 'breaks' I will need to do? 4

© CGP — not to be photocopied

11

You have **10 minutes** to do this test. Work as quickly and accurately as you can.

1. A new red carpet is needed for a film premiere.
    The carpet needs to be 12.35 m long.
    How long must the carpet be in millimetres?

     mm

2. Emily has a new bike. She needs to adjust it so that when the pedal is at its
    lowest point (as shown below), her knee makes an angle of x.

    Circle the best estimate of x from the options below.

A 70°	**C** 140°	**E** 210°	
B 90°	**(D)** 170°		

3. An asteroid travels 22 586 km every hour.
    Round this distance to the nearest thousand kilometres.

     km

4. Arno buys 5 rolls of wallpaper to decorate his kitchen.
    While decorating, he uses $3^3/_5$ rolls.
    How many rolls of wallpaper does Arno have left? Circle the correct answer.

A $^{18}/_5$	**C** $^7/_5$	**(E)** $^{13}/_5$
B $^{12}/_5$	**D** $^7/_{10}$	

5. The total area of all 6 faces of a dice is 24 cm².
    What is the length of one of the sides?

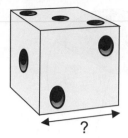

?

$24 \div 6 = 4$ cm

☒ ☐ 4 cm

6. The shape below shows a picture frame.
    The frame is a regular 10-sided shape with its centre at O.
    What is the size of the angle marked *x*?

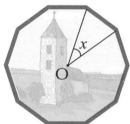

x

O

☒ ☐ 4 5 °

7. Heidi runs round her school playground on four different days.
    Her times are 65 seconds, 69 seconds, 62 seconds and 68 seconds.
    What was the mean of her times?

☐ 6 6 seconds

```
  65        196          66       66
  69         68      4 )264      × 4
 ___        ___       ─24        ───
 134        264         24       264
  62                    24
 ___                    24
 196                    00
```

8. A radio was for sale in a shop at a price of £12.
    Its price was increased by 10%.
    Its new price was then decreased by 10%.
    What is the current price of the radio?

10% of £12 = £1·20

```
 12.00
  1.20
 ─────
 10.80
```

$1.20 × 12$

£ ☐ 1 0 . 8 0

120 people were asked how many sisters they have.
The results are shown in the pie chart below.

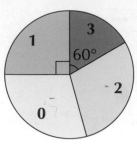

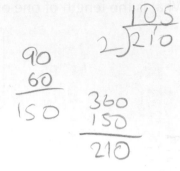

9.   How many people have 1 sister?

$\boxed{}\,\boxed{9}\,\boxed{0}$

10. 35 people have no sisters. The segment with 2 sisters is the same size as the segment with no sisters. How many more people have 2 sisters than 3 sisters? Circle the answer below.

A   35   C   15   E   105

B   25   D   5

The price (in pounds) charged by a designer for each job they carry out is 50h + 25, where h is the number of hours taken.

$50 \times h + 25$

11. What would the price be for a job that takes 30 hours?

£ $\boxed{}\,\boxed{1}\,\boxed{5}\,\boxed{2}\,\boxed{5}$

12. A customer is charged £1025.
     How many hours did the designer take to do that job?

$\boxed{}\,\boxed{2}\,\boxed{0}$ hours

$\begin{array}{r} 1025 \\ -25 \\ \hline 1000 \end{array}$

$1000 \div 50 = 20$

/ 12

You have **10 minutes** to do this test. Work as quickly and accurately as you can.

1. A triangle has two sides of length 3.8 cm and 7.4 cm, and a perimeter of 18 cm.
    Find the length of its third side.

    ☐ 6 . 8 cm ✓

2. The mile counter on a car is shown below.

    Round the distance shown to the nearest 1000 miles.

    ☐ 5 4 . 0 0 0 miles

3. The headline for a newspaper story is shown below.

    > **Nearly 2 out of every 3 people have been on a foreign holiday this year**

    The exact percentage of people who had been on a foreign holiday
    this year is given in the story.
    Circle the percentage below that best matches the headline.

A	33%	**C** 64%		**E**	73%
B	49%	**D** 67%			

4. A side view of a skateboard ramp is shown below.

    90
    90
    42
    ____
    222

    360
    $+ 222$ —
    ____
    38

    ✗

    What is the size of angle X?

    ☐ 3 8 °

5. Caley is making 7 cakes. Each cake requires 85 grams of flour.
To make the cakes, Caley uses a new 1 kg packet of flour.
How many grams of flour will be left in the packet?

$$\begin{array}{r} 85 \\ \times\ 7 \\ \hline 59\ 5 \\ 3 \end{array}$$

$\cancel{1\ 0\ 0\ 0} \rightarrow 1\ kg = 1000\ g$

$$\begin{array}{r} 595 \\ \hline 4\ 0\ 5 \end{array}$$

 4 0 5 g

6. A shipping container is $2^1/_4$ m high.
Six of these shipping containers are stacked on top of each other.
How tall is the stack? Circle the correct answer.

A   12 m   C $13^1/_4$ m   (E) $14^1/_4$ m

B $12^1/_2$ m   D $13^1/_2$ m

7. The sign below is in the shape of a rhombus.
The dotted lines are lines of symmetry.

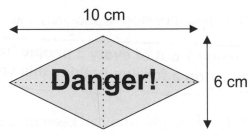

10 cm

6 cm

What is the area of the sign?

$10 \times 6 = 60$

$60 \div 4 = 15$

 1 5 cm²

8. An investor puts some money into a company. At the end of Year 1, his investment
is worth 4 times as much as it was at the start. At the end of Year 2, it was worth
2.5 times as much as at the end of Year 1.
If the original investment was £135, how much was it worth at the end of Year 2?

A   £13 500   (C)   £1350   E   £2280

B   £290   D   £1050

$$\begin{array}{r} 135 \\ \times\ 4 \\ \hline 540 \end{array}$$

$$\begin{array}{r} 540 \\ 25 \\ \hline 2700 \\ 1080 \\ \hline 1350\ 0.0 \end{array}$$

Ciara carries out a survey of the traffic passing her house.
She records the type of vehicle she sees and whether each vehicle was travelling
north or south. Her results are in this table, but some entries are missing.

	Car	Lorry	Bus	Total
North	31	7	*11*	49
South	*20*	*8*	3	*31*
Total	*51*	15	*14*	80

9.   How many buses did Ciara see?

15 + 14 = 29
80 − 29 = 51

□ 1 4

10.   What fraction of the vehicles that Ciara recorded were cars travelling south?
Circle the correct answer.

A $^1/_4$ C $^1/_3$ E $^2/_3$

B $^1/_5$ D $^2/_5$

11.   Ciara later records another 9 lorries and another 7 buses, but no extra cars.
What percentage of all the vehicles that Ciara saw were lorries?

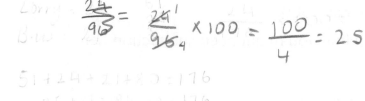

$$\frac{24}{96} = \frac{24}{96} \times 100 = \frac{100}{4} = 25$$

2 5 %

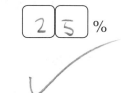

12.   A truck manufacturer says that at a speed s (in kilometres per hour), its new model
of truck takes a total distance of d metres to stop, where $d = s(^1/_{100}\,s + 1)$.
Circle the distance the truck will take to stop from a speed of 10 kilometres per hour.

A   11 metres   C   11.1 metres   E   1.1 metres

B   1 metre   D   110 metres

8 / 12

© CGP — not to be photocopied

17

Test 5

Time for a break! These puzzles are a great way to practise your maths skills.

It Doesn't Add Up

One evening, Claire and her friend Will were talking.

"I can add eight 8s together to make 1000."

"Nonsense... eight 8s added together make 64."

Claire then wrote on a piece of paper:

$$888 + 88 + 8 + 8 + 8 = 1000$$

Okay... your turn.

- Add eight 4s together to make 500. $444 + 44 + 4 + 4 + 4 = 500$

- Add sixteen 2s together to make 500. $222 + 222 + 22 + 22 + 2 + 2$ $+ 2 + 2 + 2 + 2 = 500$

- Use ten 3s to make 600. (Hint: you might need subtraction here)

   $333 + 333 - 33 - 33 = 600$

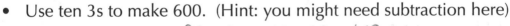

What's on the Cards?

Will now wants to test Claire.

He has a pack of numbered cards and lays a few out in front of her to make a sequence.

Okay, Clever Clogs... what's on the card that's face down?

18 98 96 101

© CGP — not to be photocopied

You have **10 minutes** to do this test. Work as quickly and accurately as you can.

1. A game of bingo starts with 90 balls in a machine. Part way through a game, 34 balls have been picked out. How many balls are left in the machine?

2. Joanne and some friends are playing a describing game. On Joanne's go, she says:

> "It is a shape with three sides. All of the angles are different, and one of them is 90°."

What is Joanne describing? Circle the correct option.

   A   Equilateral triangle

   B   Tetrahedron

   C   Right-angled triangle

   D   Triangular prism

   E   Isosceles triangle

3. Liam has seven cards, shown below. The back of each card is a different colour.

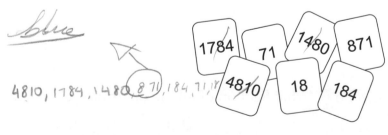

Liam places the cards in ascending order. The back of the middle card is blue. What number is on the blue card? Circle the correct option.

   A   71   **C**   1480   **E**   1784

   B   4810   **D**   871

© CGP — not to be photocopied

Test 6

4. Sandy has a jug that can hold 5 litres of water. It is $\frac{1}{4}$ full.
She pours 400 ml away. How much water is left in the jug, in millilitres?

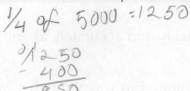

$\frac{1}{4}$ of 5000 = 1250

$\cancel{1250}$
$-\ 400$
$\overline{\ 850}$

| 8 | 5 | 0 | ml

The colours of the front doors in a block of flats are shown in a bar chart below.

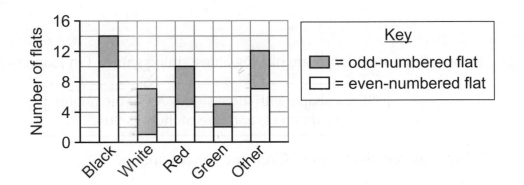

5. Which is the most common colour of front door for odd-numbered flats?
Circle the correct option.

    A   Black   **C**   Red   **E**   Can't say

    B   White   **D**   Green

6. Each floor of the block is 3.5 m tall. There is exactly one flat with a white front
door on each floor of the block. How tall is the block of flats?

3.5
$\times\ 7$
$\overline{24.5}$

| 2 | 4 | . | 5 | m

7. $\frac{2}{3}$ of the 'Other' doors are yellow. What fraction of all the doors are yellow?
Circle the correct option.

    A $\frac{1}{12}$ **C** $\frac{1}{6}$ **E** $\frac{1}{7}$

    B $\frac{2}{15}$ **D** $\frac{1}{8}$

8. A motor spins 77 times per second. How many times does it spin in 3 minutes and 24 seconds? Circle the correct option.

A   28 046   C   1592   E   161 478

B   15 708   D   24 948

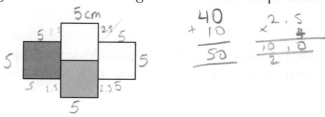

3 mins → 180 sec
24 secs → 24 sec
180
+ 24
304

Lily has square tiles with side length 5 cm. She arranges them in the shape shown below.

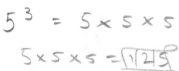

40
+ 10
50

2.5
× 4
10 0

9. What is the perimeter of Lily's shape?

5 0 cm

10. Lily adds three more squares to her shape. What is the area of the new shape?

$5^3 = 5 \times 5 \times 5$

$5 \times 5 \times 5 = \boxed{125}$

1 2 5 cm²

11. Daffyd is saving money for a new camera. In Week 1 he puts £50 into the bank. Each week, the amount he puts into the bank <u>halves</u>. In which week does the amount that Daffyd wants to put into the bank <u>contain half a penny</u>?

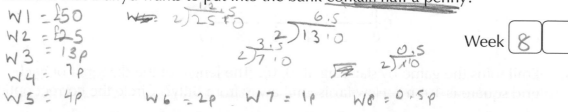

W1 = £50
W2 = £25
W3 = 13p
W4 = 7p
W5 = 4p   W6 = 2p   W7 = 1p   W8 = 0.5p

Week 8

12. Terri is x years old. Selma is 5 years older than Terri, and Karl is twice as old as Selma. How old is Karl, in terms of x? Circle the correct option.

A   2(x + 5)   C   2x + 7   E   5x + 2

B   2x + 5   D   2(2x + 5)

/ 12

© CGP — not to be photocopied

21

Test 6

You have **10 minutes** to do this test. Work as quickly and accurately as you can.

1. A sailor needs a piece of rope that measures 4.3 m, to the nearest 0.1 m.
    What is the shortest possible length of rope that the sailor can have?

     5 . 1 ⬜ m

2. A new novel costs £8.00. An edition signed by the author costs
    2.5 times the normal price. How much does the signed edition cost?

    £  2 4 . 0 0

Ann, Billy, Cris and Dai are playing a playground game on a grid.
Their positions are shown by their initials on the diagram below.

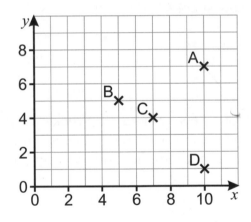

3. Emil joins the game by standing at (0, 0). The length of the diagonal of each
    grid square is 1.4 m. How far is Emil away from Billy? Circle the correct option.

A 8.8 m	**C** 7 m	**E** 9.8 m
B 4.6 m	**D** 11.2 m	

    1·4 × 5 = 7.0 m

4. Emil must now move to a different position, so that
    he's an equal distance from each of Ann, Cris and Dai.
    At what coordinates should Emil stand?

     (1 2 , 0 4)

5. Tamal is making apple tarts. For the pastry, he mixes together 250 g of flour and 300 g of butter. He makes ten identical pastry cases from this with none left over, and fills each one with 30 g of filling. What is the mass of each tart? Circle the correct option.

250
+300
550 g

   A   580 g   C   850 g   E   85 g
   B   80 g   D   58 g

6. Layla records the number of train journeys she goes on each year for five years. The results are shown in the table.

Year	2011	2012	2013	2014	2015
No. train journeys	26	14	17	20	23

What is the mean number of train journeys that Layla went on each year during this period?

26
14
17 +
20
23
100

100 ÷ 5 = 20
20 × 5 = 100

7. An A4 piece of paper is 297 mm long and 210 mm wide. Jaime wants to cut out squares with side length 50 mm. What is the maximum number of squares that Jaime can cut out from an A4 piece of paper?

297 +
210
507
1

507 ÷ 4 =
126.75
4)507 → 127
       - 50
       77

8. Wolfgang runs a marathon in 3 hours 40 minutes. Liza takes 10% longer to run the marathon than Wolfgang. How long does it take Liza to run the marathon? Circle the correct option.

3 hrs → 180 mins
40 mins → 40 mins
220

   A   3 hours 18 minutes
   B   3 hours 58 minutes
   C   4 hours 2 minutes
   D   4 hours 28 minutes
   E   5 hours 2 minutes

10/220 × 100 = 10/22 =

220
- 10
210

9. As part of a design project, Rashida cuts pieces of fabric into the shapes shown below.

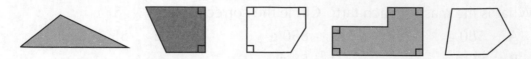

She then counts the number of obtuse angles on each shape.
What is the most common number of obtuse angles?

A standard piano has 52 white keys and 36 black keys. Mr Joel is a piano repairman.
He is repairing a piano where $^1/_{13}$ of the white keys and $^1/_3$ of the black keys are missing.

10. How many keys are missing in total?

$^1/_{13}$ of $52 = 4$

$^1/_3$ of $36 = 12$

$\begin{array}{r} 12 \\ + 4 \\ \hline 16 \end{array}$

11. What fraction of the remaining keys are black? Circle the correct option.

A $^1/_9$ C $^1/_3$ E $^1/_8$
B $^1/_{13}$ D $^1/_5$

12. White keys cost £3, and black keys cost £2.
What is the formula for the price of x white keys and y black keys? Circle the correct option.

A $3(x + y) + 2$
B $3y + 2x$
C $3x + 2y$
D $5(y + x)$
E $3xy + 2xy$

/ 12

© CGP — not to be photocopied

You have **10 minutes** to do this test. Work as quickly and accurately as you can.

1. A clock says that the time is 3:16 pm. It is 20 minutes fast. What is the correct time?

 $0\ 3:3\ 6$ pm

A signpost in Pubbley shows the distances, in kilometres, to five nearby villages.

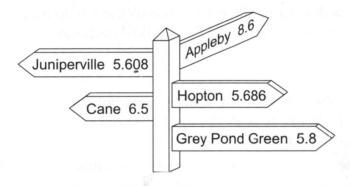

Appleby 8.6

Juniperville 5.608

Hopton 5.686

Cane 6.5

Grey Pond Green 5.8

2. Which is the closest village to Pubbley? Circle the correct option.

A Appleby   **C** Hopton   **E** Grey Pond Green

B Juniperville   **D** Cane

3. Grey Pond Green is directly East of Pubbley, and Cane is directly West.
    What is the distance between Grey Pond Green and Cane?

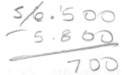

6.500
– 5.800
_____
   700

 $0.7\ 0$ km

4. A delivery service charges £1.50 for every kilogram that a parcel weighs,
    where a parcel's weight is always rounded up to the next whole kilogram.
    How much does it cost to deliver a parcel that weighs 4384 g?

£

The graph below shows how the height above sea level of a popular walking route changes along its length.

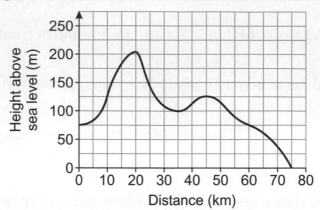

5. A group of walkers took three days to walk the whole route.
What is the mean distance that they walked each day?

⬜⬜⬜ km

6. On the downhill sections, the walkers were going at 3 km/h.
How long did it take to walk the long downhill section at the end of the route?
Circle the correct option.

    A   5 hours   **C**   8 hours 30 minutes   **E**   15 hours
    B   10 hours   **D**   12 hours 30 minutes

7. Pop Factory is a 4-member boy band. Their new calendar contains 12 photos.
Each member of the band has two photos in the calendar featuring just them.
The other photos feature the whole band. What fraction of the photos feature the whole band? Circle the correct option.

    A $^1/_{12}$ **C** $^1/_3$ **E** $^1/_2$
    B $^2/_3$ **D** $^1/_6$

8. Gina has three circular cards, each with an area of 25 cm². She places them in a figure, as shown below, so that each overlap has an area of 5 cm².

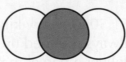

What is the area of the figure?

⬜⬜⬜ cm²

9. Kayleigh stands facing North. She turns 150° clockwise, then 90° anticlockwise, then 30° clockwise. Which direction is she now facing? Circle the correct option.

A East   **C** North   **E** West

B North East   **D** North West

$150 + 30 = 180°$

$W \longrightarrow E$ $S - 90° = E$ $N \longrightarrow S$

A car salesperson wants to increase the number of cars she has in her showroom. Each week she sells five cars, and then at the end of the week she buys enough cars to double her remaining stock.

10. In Week 1 she starts with 15 cars. In which week will she start with over 40 cars in her showroom?

Week [3][ ]

11. A rival car salesperson also sells five cars per week, and also decides to double his stock at the end of each week. If in Week 1 he starts with 10 cars in his showroom, how many cars will he have at the start of Week 18? Circle the correct option.

A 0   **C** 1 310 725   **E** 17 995

B 175   **D** 10

12. In a woodwork exam, a student is given a 10 cm cube of wood and cuts a 2 cm cube from each corner, as shown below.

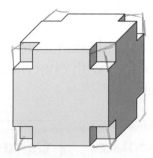

What is the volume of this shape? Circle the correct option.

A 936 cm³   **C** 36 cm³   **E** 640 cm³

B 1064 cm³   **D** 128 cm³

/ 12

© CGP — not to be photocopied

Time for a break! These puzzles are a great way to practise your maths skills.

Pipe Dreams

A chocolate factory makes two caramel bars, CaraMini and CaraMax.
They are made in separate rooms, but the chocolate and caramel come via pipes
from a Chocolate supply and a Caramel supply.
To avoid any mix-up, none of the pipes can cross over each other.

- Can you draw four pipes on the plan that allow both rooms to get
  chocolate and caramel?

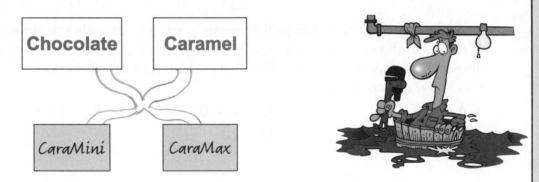

- A new caramel bar, MegaCaramel, is created and will be made in a new room.
  Can the chocolate and caramel be supplied to all three rooms with no pipes
  crossing over? Yes

- A Peanut supply is created to add peanuts to all three bars.
  Can all three rooms be supplied with chocolate, caramel and peanuts,
  without pipes crossing over?

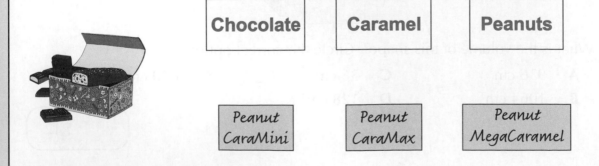

You have **10 minutes** to do this test. Work as quickly and accurately as you can.

1. Two litres of water drip into a container every hour. The container is full after 2 whole days. What is the capacity of the container?

 2 4 litres

2. A wrestler wins 4 fights in April, 9 in May, 8 in June, and 11 in July. What is the mean number of fights he wins per month in this period?

[ ] 6

3. Roger finds a weed in his garden that is 11.7 cm tall. When he digs it up, he finds that the roots are 65 mm long. How long is the weed in total, in centimetres? Circle the correct answer.

A	5.2 cm	**C**	17.2 cm	**E**	76.7 cm
B	7.67 cm	**D**	18.2 cm		

4. A factory makes dummies. It costs 1p to make each dummy. The factory then sells them to shops in packs of 100 for £10. How much profit does the factory make on each pack of dummies?

£[ ].[ ][ ]

5. Kazuo is moving to a new house, 2 km away from his old house. He has 12 boxes of belongings to move in total, but he can only fit 4 boxes into his car. What is the shortest distance that he has to drive to get all of his boxes to his new house?

 6 km

6. A coat usually costs £40. One coat has a fault, so the price is reduced by 65%. How much does the faulty coat cost?

£ 1 4 . 0 0

The map below shows a bay with two lighthouses, A and B.

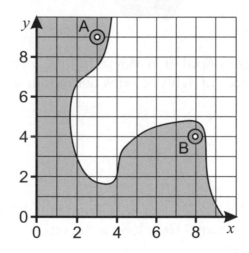

7. Lighthouse A shines on Lighthouse B every 11 seconds.
Lighthouse B shines on Lighthouse A every 8 seconds.
They start off shining on each other.
How long will it be till they are both shining on each other again?

 1 9 seconds

8. A third lighthouse is built six squares left and two squares down from B on the map. What are the coordinates of the third lighthouse? Circle the correct option.

A (2, 2)   C (1, 2)   E (2, 1)

B (1, 3)   D (2, 3)

9. The path through the Forest of Dyelem starts off as one path, then splits into two. Both of these split into five paths, and each of these splits again into two paths. All the paths end at different places. How many end places are there?

The box shown below is used to store identical 10 cm cubes.

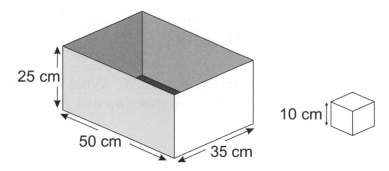

25 cm

50 cm

35 cm

10 cm

10. How many cubes can fit completely inside the box?

11. When there is one cube in the box, the total mass is 150 g.
When there are seven cubes in the box, the total mass is 750 g.
What is the mass of the box? Circle the correct option.

A   50 g   C   75 g   E   125 g
B   70 g   D   100 g

12. Davina wins some money. She gives 20% of it to her brother, Dale. Dale splits his share equally between his three children. What fraction of Davina's winnings do each of Dale's children get? Circle the correct option.

A $^1/_{24}$ C $^3/_{20}$ E $^1/_{15}$
B $^3/_5$ D $^3/_{25}$

/ 12

© CGP — not to be photocopied

31

You have **10 minutes** to do this test. Work as quickly and accurately as you can.

A stall at a bake sale sells jam tarts for 25p each.

1. Geli buys 5 jam tarts with a £2 coin. How much change should Geli get?
    Circle the correct option.

    A   £1.25   **C**   75p   **E**   25p

    B   25p   **D**   £1

2. At the end of the day, the stall has made £36.50. What is the smallest
    total number of coins and notes that can make up this amount?

     5

3. One of the windows on a house is in the shape of an irregular quadrilateral.
    Three of the corners are angles of 70°. What is the size of the fourth angle?

    150 °

    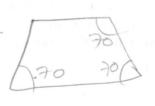

Jack was born on Saturday 25th July 2015 and weighed 5 pounds and 8 ounces.

4. There are 16 ounces in 1 pound.
    How many ounces did Jack weigh when he was born?

    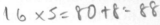

    $16 \times 5 = 80 + 8 = 88$

    8 8 oz

5. He was taken for a check-up on the 14th August 2015.
    What day of the week was Jack's check-up? Circle the correct option.

    A   Monday   **C**   Wednesday   **E**   Friday

    B   Tuesday   **D**   Thursday

6. A cube has a corner cut off to form two new shapes, as shown below.

What is the total number of faces on the two new shapes?

7. Ekatarina catches a fish that's 42 cm long. This is 6 times longer than her smallest ever catch, and 8 cm shorter than her biggest ever catch. What's the difference in length between her biggest and smallest ever catches? Circle the correct option.

A   14 cm   C   46 cm   E   244 cm
B   43 cm   D   53 cm

8. The prices of houses on sale in a village are shown in a bar chart below.

The Joneses want to buy a house in the village for less than £200 000.
What fraction of the houses on sale can they afford? Circle the correct option.

A $^1/_3$ C $^2/_3$ E $^4/_9$
B $^1/_9$ D $^1/_2$

Lenia is making a mosaic using triangular tiles. Each day she adds one row to the mosaic. The diagrams below show the mosaic on the first four days.

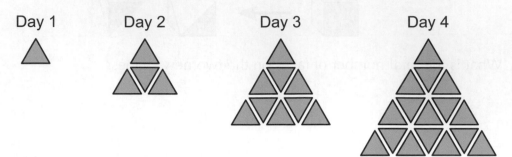

Day 1   Day 2   Day 3   Day 4

9.   How many tiles will Lenia add to the pattern on Day 5?

10.   How many tiles will there be in the mosaic on Day 10? Circle the correct option.

   A   20   **C**   88   **E**   250
   B   50   **D**   100

11.   A round cake is shared between Abi, Elvera and Tina. The angle cut at the centre of the cake for each piece is that person's age multiplied by 10. Abi is 9 years old and Elvera is 14 years old. How old is Tina?

12.   One side of a street has just odd-numbered houses. Lydia and Atif live next door to each other on this side of the street, and both their house numbers are prime. When added together, their house numbers make a square number less than 50. What are their two house numbers?

 and

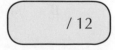

/ 12

Time for a break! These puzzles are a great way to practise your maths skills.

T, Cut

Trace over the four shapes on the left and carefully cut them out.
Can you arrange them into the 'T' shape shown on the right?

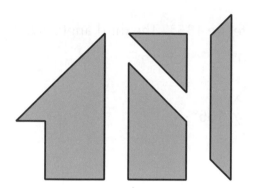 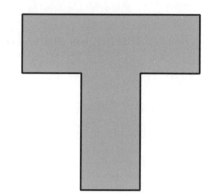

Fake or Fortune?

Joseph was digging in his garden and came across two very old vases.
He knew they were very old, because on the bottom was carved
the date, month and year that they were made.

XXXI · III   XXXI · VII
MCLI   MXCXI

Joseph showed them to his friend Gina, who's something of an expert.
As soon as she looked at them, she said, "I can't date one of them —
it could be a fake." Which one?

© CGP — not to be photocopied

⏱ 10

You have **10 minutes** to do this test. Work as quickly and accurately as you can.

1. There are 21 pupils in class 6H. Each pupil has eight colouring pencils.
   How many colouring pencils are there in total?

   `1 6 8`

2. Two of the angles at the corners of Suzie's kite are 135°. The third angle is 60°.

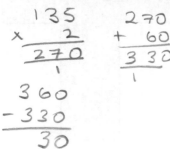

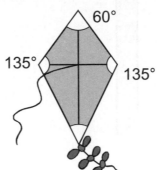

   What is the size of the fourth angle?

   `3 0`°

On Monday Jai ate 28.7 g of cheese. On Tuesday he had 26.9 g, on Wednesday he had 42.7 g, on Thursday he had 37.8 g and on Friday he had 23.9 g of cheese.

3. Jai writes out his measurements in order of size, from lightest to heaviest.
   Which value is in the middle of the list? Circle the correct option.

   (A) 28.7 g   C   42.7 g   E   23.9 g
   B   26.9 g   D   37.8 g

4. In total, Jai ate 160 g of cheese in the five days from Monday to Friday.
   On Saturday, he had 26 g of cheese, and on Sunday he ate 24 g of cheese.
   What is the mean mass of cheese that he ate each day that week?

   `3 0` g

5.   A playground is in the shape of a regular pentagon. Each side is 9.08 m long.
     What is the perimeter of the playground?

     9.08
   ×   5
   ─────
   45.40

   $\boxed{4}\boxed{5}.\boxed{4}\boxed{0}$ m

6.   Steve bought 14 salads with a £20 note and received six pounds in change.
     How much would 70 salads cost to buy?

   £ $\boxed{1}\boxed{1}\boxed{4}$

7.   Clara saw this message at the end of her favourite television show.

   This episode was made in the year
   MMXIII

   The first series was made eight years before the episode that Clara saw.
   In what year was the first series made? Circle the correct option.

   A   MMXXI   **C**   MCMXCV   **E**   VIII
   B   MXV   (**D**) MMV

8.   Ayaan draws a rectangle on the coordinate grid below.
     Its corners are at (3, 0), (7, 0), (7, 6) and (3, 6).
     What are the coordinates of the centre of the rectangle?

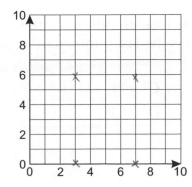

   ($\boxed{0}\boxed{5}$, $\boxed{0}\boxed{3}$)

© CGP — not to be photocopied   37   Test 11

9. A book is 20 cm wide, 25 cm tall and 0.5 cm thick.
    Three copies of this book are stacked neatly on a shelf in a bookshop.
    What is the total volume of all three copies of the book?

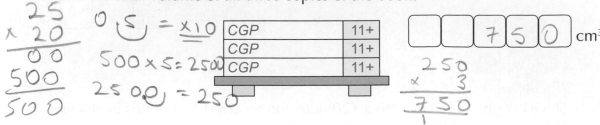

$$\begin{array}{r} 2\,5 \\ \times\ 2\,0 \\ \hline 0\,0 \\ 5\,0\,0 \\ \hline 5\,0\,0 \end{array}$$

$0.5 = \times 10$

$500 \times 5 = 2500$

$2500 \;\) = 250$

$$\begin{array}{r} 2\,5\,0 \\ \times\ \ \ 3 \\ \hline 7\,5\,0 \end{array}$$

☐ ☐ 7 5 0 cm³

Mike is filling party bags for the guests at his birthday party. He puts three boxes of sweets in each party bag — but he always eats two sweets from each party bag.

10. Each box of sweets contains x sweets. What is the expression for the number of sweets in each party bag? Circle the correct answer.

    A $2x - 3$ **C** $2x + 3$ **E** $2 - 3x$

    B $3x - 2$ **(D)** $3 - 2x$

11. In total, there are 25 sweets in each party bag. 20% of the sweets in each party bag are Chocolate Twigs. 40% of the sweets are Chewy Fruits. The rest are hard-boiled mints. How many hard-boiled mints are there in each party bag?

$25\ sw$

$20\% = 5$

$40\% = 10\ ^+$

$\overline{(15)}$ $25 - 15 = (10)$

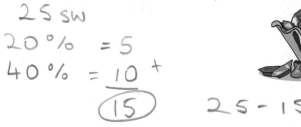

☐ ☐

12. Ann wants to make as many prime numbers as possible by making piles of marbles. She starts with the smallest prime number, has 50 marbles and doesn't re-use them. What is the last prime number she can make?
    Circle the correct answer.

    A   5   **C**   11   **E**   17

    (B) 7   **D**   13

/ 12

             © CGP — not to be photocopied

You have **10 minutes** to do this test. Work as quickly and accurately as you can.

1. A volcano last erupted eleven-thousand nine-hundred and eighty-two years ago. What is this number rounded to the nearest hundred years?

    11,982

Carly is making a triangular sail for a pretend boat to use in a play. The sail is 6 m wide and 3 m tall, and costs £45 to make.

2. What is the area of Carly's sail?

    ☐☐ m²

3. Each square metre of a sail costs the same amount to make. Carly makes another sail that is $\frac{1}{3}$ the area of the first sail. How much does this cost?

    £☐☐.☐☐

4. The number of snails in Mia's garden changes by the same amount each day. On Monday there were 21 snails, on Tuesday there were 19 snails, on Wednesday there were 17 snails and on Thursday there were 15 snails. How many snails will there be on Saturday?

A	13		**C**	14	**E**	12
B	10		**D**	11		

5. Billy's bookshelves are 0.8 metres long. He puts up three in a row. How many millimetres wide in total are Billy's bookshelves? Circle the correct answer.

   A 2400 mm   **C** 240 000 mm   **E** 24 000 000 mm

   B 24 000 mm   **D** 2 400 000 mm

6. When Ava divides her t-shirts into 11 piles, she has nine t-shirts in every pile. How many t-shirts will be in each pile if she divides her t-shirts into just three piles instead?

7. Stripy fabric costs £11.20 per metre at a fabric shop. Sim buys 386.8 m of fabric to decorate his school's hall. What is the total cost of the fabric? Circle the correct option.

   A   £433 216

   B   £433.21

   C   £43.32

   D   £4332.16

   E   £43 321.60

8. $^1/_3$ of the songs on Nic's favourite playlist are pop songs. $^1/_5$ are rap songs, and the rest are rock songs. What fraction of songs on Nic's playlist are rock songs? Circle the correct option.

   A $^2/_5$

   B $^8/_{15}$

   C $^2/_8$

   D $^7/_{15}$

   E $^3/_5$

Chris asked 40 pupils how they got to school in the morning.
He used their answers to draw the pie chart below.

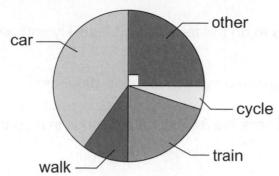

9. Four-fifths of the pupils who said 'other' took the bus to school.
    How many pupils took the bus?

10. 4 pupils walked to school. What percentage arrived by car?

 %

11. Ellie's collection of toy cars can be divided into groups of 3, 4, 5 or 15 cars
    without any cars being left over. Which of the numbers below could be the
    number of cars in Ellie's collection? Circle the correct option.

    A   40   **C**   60   **E**   45
    B   27   **D**   15

12. Pavel earns pocket money by washing dishes. He earns £1.75 when he starts
    washing up, then he earns an extra 35p for every dish he washes.
    Which of the expressions below can be used to calculate the amount of pocket
    money Pavel earns in pounds when he washes d dishes? Circle the correct option.

    A $35d + 1.75$ **C** $175d + 35$ **E** $0.35(d + 1.75)$
    B $1.75 + 0.35d$ **D** $35d + 175$

/ 12

© CGP — not to be photocopied

Test 12

You have **10 minutes** to do this test. Work as quickly and accurately as you can.

The sentence below appeared in a school book about time.

> There are 31 536 000 seconds in a year.

1.   In the sentence, what does the number 5 represent? Circle the correct option.

    A   five hundred million   **D**   five hundred thousand

    B   fifty million   **E**   fifty thousand

    C   five million

2.   How many whole years are there in one hundred million seconds?

                                                □□ years

3.   Maja's wardrobe contains 5 blue shirts, 3 red shirts, 9 purple jumpers
    and 3 brown jumpers. What is the ratio of shirts to jumpers?
    Give your answer in its simplest form.

                                               □□ : □□

4.   Imagine a diagonal line going from the bottom-left corner of this page to the
    top-right corner of the next page. Estimate the angle between the bottom of this
    page and the diagonal line. Circle the best option.

    A   300°   **C**   180°   **E**   30°

    B   270°   **D**   90°

A bus timetable is shown below.

High Street	0702	0839	0954	1109
West Hill	0710	0848	0959	1121
Hillcrest Road	0720	0900	1008	1134

5. How long is the longest journey between High Street and West Hill?

    [   ] minutes

6. What is the mean time the bus takes to travel from West Hill to Hillcrest Road
    on the four journeys shown?

    [   ] minutes

7. Caleb is painting a fence. He painted 24.6 m² of fence and used 3 litres of paint.
    What area of fence could he paint with 150 litres of paint?
    Circle the correct answer.

    A   123 m²
    B   246 m²
    C   1230 m²
    D   2460 m²
    E   12 300 m²

8. A mosaic contains green and blue cuboid-shaped tiles. All the tiles are 5 cm long,
    4 cm wide and 0.5 cm thick. Andy stacks 25 green tiles and 13 blue tiles together
    in a tall pile. What is the total volume of the pile?

    [   ] cm³

9. Nadia tossed an unfair coin 480 times. It landed heads one-sixth of the time. How many times did it land tails?

10. A lawn has the shape of a right-angled triangle. It is 16 m long and 21 m wide. A tub of grass feed is enough to fertilise 30 m² of lawn. How many tubs of grass feed are needed to fertilise the entire lawn? Circle the correct option.

   A   112
   B   5
   C   6
   D   11
   E   12

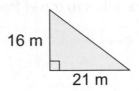

16 m

21 m

11. On Monday, Char thought of a number. Each day after that she multiplied the previous day's number by 3. She started with the number –2.
On which day was the number first less than –40? Circle the correct option.

   A   Wednesday
   B   Thursday
   C   Friday
   D   Saturday
   E   The sequence will never be less than –40

12. There are 240 children in Year 6. Exactly $\frac{1}{3}$ of the children are boys, the rest are girls. $\frac{1}{4}$ of the boys have green eyes. $\frac{3}{8}$ of the girls have green eyes. How many children in Year 6 have green eyes?

/ 12

Time for a break! These puzzles are a great way to practise your maths skills.

Abracadabra?

Barry really, really wants to go to wizard school.

The trouble is, he isn't very magical at all.
The best he can do is chuck a 3-eyed frog about.

If he can fill in the grid below so that the letters of the word
"WIZARD" appear once in every row and column, he might
just turn into a wizard and toddle off to wizard school.

Can you help him?

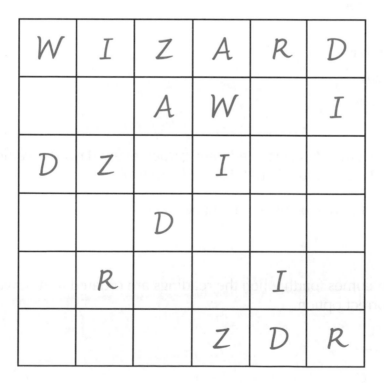

W	I	Z	A	R	D
		A	W		I
D	Z		I		
		D			
	R			I	
			Z	D	R

© CGP — not to be photocopied

You have **10 minutes** to do this test. Work as quickly and accurately as you can.

1. A big group of pupils travelled to and from an island.
   On the way there, 220 pupils took a red ferry and 200 took a blue ferry.
   On the way back, 235 pupils took the red ferry and the rest took the blue ferry.
   How many pupils took the blue ferry on the way back?

2. Olga counts the number of stickers in her collection each day.
   On the first day, Olga has 20 smiley face stickers. On the second day she gives
   away three stickers. Each day she gives away three more stickers. After which day
   will she have fewer than 10 stickers left? Circle the correct option.

   A   Second day
   B   Third day
   C   Fourth day
   D   Fifth day
   E   Sixth day

Ash recorded the average temperature in her garden every day. The values she recorded
were 3.43 °C, 2.92 °C, –1.96 °C, 4.20 °C, and –2.80 °C.

3. What is the difference between the highest and lowest value Ash recorded?

    °C

4. Which value comes fourth when the readings are ordered from lowest to highest?
   Circle the correct option.

   A   3.43 °C
   B   2.92 °C
   C   –1.96 °C
   D   4.20 °C
   E   –2.80 °C

5. A building is in the shape of a regular heptagon. Its perimeter is 252 m.
    What is the length of each side?

     m

6. Doug built a gatehouse for his model castle using 17 cuboid blocks. Each block is
    2 cm wide, 1 cm tall and 3 cm deep. What is the volume of the gatehouse?

    cm³

7. Elodie asked 45 pupils in Year 5 if they have a pet. She recorded their responses
    on the bar chart. No pupil had more than one pet.

    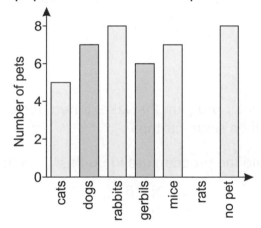

    Elodie forgot to draw the bar for rats. How many pupils have a rat?

8. A car travels 54.1 miles for each gallon of fuel it uses. It used 8.76 gallons of fuel
    on a journey. Estimate how far it travelled on the journey.
    Circle the correct option.

    A   473.916 miles   **C**   386.201 miles   **E**   340.537 miles
    B   601.378 miles   **D**   404.935 miles

Martha used 36 eggs and 18 kg of flour to make 48 cakes.

9. How many eggs and how much flour will she need to make 8 cakes?
   Circle the correct option.

   A 11 eggs and 21 kg of flour
   B 6 eggs and 4 kg of flour
   C 21 eggs and 11 kg of flour
   D 3 eggs and 6 kg of flour
   E 6 eggs and 3 kg of flour

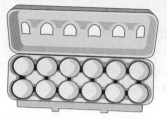

10. Martha took her 48 cakes to a cake sale. She sold $\frac{1}{3}$ of the cakes for 80p each
    and the rest of the cakes for £1.00 each. How much money did she make?

    £ ⬜⬜.⬜⬜

Leon wrote a simple computer program that takes a number, n,
multiplies it by three and then subtracts three.

11. What expression could the program use to do this? Circle the correct option.

    A $2n$ C $n + 3$ E $3n + 3$
    B $2n + 1$ D $3n - 3$

12. The program returned the number 36. What number did Leon enter?

    ⬜⬜

/ 12

© CGP — not to be photocopied

You have **10 minutes** to do this test. Work as quickly and accurately as you can.

1. Tim travels from Lancaster to Birmingham by train. His train leaves Lancaster at 13:58 and arrives in Birmingham at 16:14. How long does his journey take?

 hours  minutes

2. A plank is 0.3048 metres wide. Round the width of the plank to the nearest hundredth of a metre.

. m

3. Riverton Valley Giants football club scored 63 goals last season. Ben scored 14 of these goals. What fraction of the club's goals did Ben score? Circle the correct option.

   A $^2/_7$
   B $^2/_9$
   C $^1/_7$
   D $^1/_9$
   E $^3/_7$

4. A young rabbit weighs 800 g. Its weight increases by 30%. What is its new weight? Circle the correct answer.

   A   2.4 kg
   B   1.4 kg
   C   1.04 kg
   D   0.14 kg
   E   0.104 kg

5. A cinema sells all its tickets at the same price. One evening it sold 190 tickets for a total of £1330. On the night of a big film release it sold 3800 tickets. How much money in total did the cinema sell the tickets for on that night? Circle the correct option.

   A   £26 600

   B   £13 300

   C   £2660

   D   £13 500

   E   £26 500

6. A group of builders place a rectangular section of stage measuring 10 m by 33 m next to a square section of stage with side length 9 m. What is the total area of the combined stages?

    m²

7. Agnita wants to move a shed in her garden. A plan of her garden is shown below.

   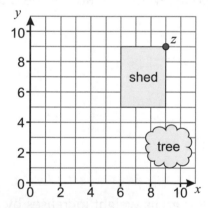

   On the grid, she moves the position of the shed five squares left and two squares down. What are the new coordinates of the corner marked z?

   (☐☐ , ☐☐)

8. Rufus is cutting a pie for his family. His two aunts would like 51° of pie each, his sister asks for 38° and his dad asks for 60°. How much of the pie is left for Rufus?

   ☐☐☐ °

Gerald is planting some seeds. He plants 42 carrot seeds and 39 cabbage seeds. Exactly $^1/_6$ of the carrot seeds and $^3/_{13}$ of the cabbage seeds grow.

9. How many plants does Gerald end up with?

10. In total, what fraction of the seeds that he planted actually grew?
    Circle the correct option.

    A $^4/_{19}$ **C** $^9/_{13}$ **E** $^{16}/_{81}$

    B $^4/_{81}$ **D** $^{16}/_{19}$

11. Gerald needs 1200 carrot plants. He thinks the same fraction of seeds will grow. How many carrot seeds should he plant in total?

12. Square pieces of decking are cut in half to make six right-angled triangles.
    A triangle of decking is placed along each side of a regular hexagonal pool.

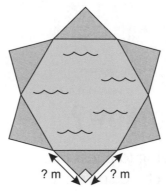

? m   ? m

    The total area of the decking is 27 m².
    How long are the short sides of the decking? Circle the correct answer.

    A 1 m   **C** 3 m   **E** 5 m

    B 2 m   **D** 4 m

/ 12

© CGP — not to be photocopied

51

Test 15

Time for a break! These puzzles are a great way to practise your maths skills.

Daylight Robbery

Stan the train driver forgot to bring a packed lunch to work, so he has to make do with the station's vending machine.

The vending machine sells drinks for £1.10 and cereal bars for 75p.
It **doesn't give change**, and it can only sell **one item** per transaction.

Stan has two 10p coins, three 20p coins, four 50p coins and two £2 coins.

He buys two drinks and as many
cereal bars as possible.
How many cereal bars can he buy?

How Old Are You Now?

Alice, Ben and Carina are trying to guess each others' ages.
They know one fact about each person's age:

- Ben's age is five times an even prime number.
- Alice is 25% older than Carina.
- Carina is two years younger than Ben.

How old are Alice, Ben and Carina?

🕙(10)

You have **10 minutes** to do this test. Work as quickly and accurately as you can.

1.   Kate's dinner plates have six long sides and two short sides.
     What shape are Kate's dinner plates? Circle the correct option.

    A   Heptagon   **C**   Pentagon   **E**   Square

    B   Octagon   **D**   Hexagon

2.   Yasmin shares 75 sweets equally between 12 people.
     How many sweets are left over?

3.   Square bathroom tiles are 25 cm wide. Two tiles are placed next to each other to
     make a rectangle. What is the perimeter of the rectangle?

    cm

4.   Nigel wants to organise the ingredients in his kitchen by mass.

He arranges them in ascending order from left to right.
Which ingredient will be second from the left? Circle the correct option.

    A   Butter   **C**   Flour   **E**   Frozen peas

    B   Mayo   **D**   Beans

5. The ratio of pens to pencils in Gavin's pencil case is 2:7. The combined total of pens and pencils is 36. How many pens does he have? Circle the correct option.

    A 8   **C** 4   **E** 72
    B 12   **D** 28

6. Karen played 45 tennis matches and won 27 of them. What fraction of games did she win? Circle the correct answer.

    A $^4/_5$
    B $^2/_3$
    C $^3/_5$
    D $^1/_2$
    E $^3/_9$

7. A line painted inside a piece of scientific equipment is 0.1397 cm wide and 1000 cm long. What is the area of the line?

    ☐☐☐☐.☐☐ cm²

8. A potter makes 120 bowls from 30 kg of clay without any clay left over. How many bowls can she complete from 2.2 kg of clay?

    ☐☐☐

Harold walks 2100 m before breakfast every day.

9. How far does Harold walk before breakfast in a year?
    Use estimation to circle the best option below.

    A 890.7 km   **C** 78.5 km   **E** 89.5 km

    B 604.5 km   **D** 766.5 km

10. One day he walks 20% further than normal.
    How far does he walk on this day?

 m

A new band released a single which sold well in the first week.
The number of people buying the band's single decreased by 50% each week.
They sold 1000 copies in the fourth week since the single was released.

11. How many copies did they sell in the first week?

12. The next single sells 1000 copies in the first week. The number of
    sales in each week after that can be found by doubling the previous
    week's sales and then adding 500. In which week after its release will
    weekly sales first be greater than 7000? Circle the correct answer.

    A 2nd week   **C** 4th week   **E** 6th week

    B 3rd week   **D** 5th week

/ 12

© CGP — not to be photocopied

Test 16

You have **10 minutes** to do this test. Work as quickly and accurately as you can.

1. A presenter announces that the winner in a lottery has won two-hundred and seven thousand and fifty-eight pounds. What is this number written in figures?

£ ☐☐☐☐☐☐

2. Mandy and Paul are reading the same book. Mandy has read 421 pages and has 389 to go. Paul has read 414 pages. How many pages does Paul have to go? Circle the correct answer.

    A   446
    B   382
    C   421
    D   414
    E   396

Quentin adds 1000 ml of orange juice and 450 ml of mango juice to 1.5 litres of water to make a tropical juice drink.

3. What is the ratio of orange juice to water? Circle the correct answer.

    A   1 : 2
    B   2 : 1
    C   3 : 2
    D   2 : 3
    E   3 : 1

4. How much tropical juice drink does Quentin make?

    ☐.☐☐ litres

Three cuboid-shaped temporary buildings are arranged in the shape below.
Each building is 10 m long, 4 m wide and 3 m tall.

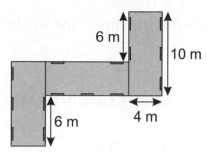

5.   What is the perimeter of the three temporary buildings as they are arranged?
     Circle the correct answer.

| **A** | 84 m | **C** | 64 m | **E** | 68 m |
| **B** | 76 m | **D** | 80 m | | |

6.   What is the total volume of the temporary buildings?

 m³

7.   The buildings need to be moved and rearranged. The builder plots the temporary
     buildings on a coordinate grid to help.

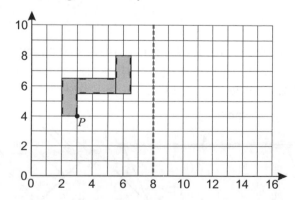

The arrangement and position of the buildings will be reflected along the dashed
mirror line. What will be the new coordinates of the point marked *P*?

(⬚⬚ , ⬚⬚)

© CGP — not to be photocopied   57   Test 17

Kellie measured the amount of rain that fell in her garden each month for four months. The values she recorded were 112 mm, 127 mm, 119 mm and 126 mm.

8. What is the difference between the largest and smallest value she recorded?

 mm

9. What is the mean of Kellie's monthly rainfall measurements?
    Circle the correct answer.

    A   118.5 mm   **C**   121 mm   **E**   116 mm

    B   123.5 mm   **D**   96.8 mm

A rectangular wall being decorated is 3 m tall and 12 m long.

10. Harry has wallpapered half of it. What area has he wallpapered?

 m²

11. Harry uses one roll of wallpaper to cover every 3.1 m² of wall. What's the smallest number of rolls of wallpaper he needs in total to decorate the wall?
    Circle the correct answer.

    A   12   **C**   7   **E**   11

    B   9   **D**   10

12. Leanne is moving house. After a company moves her furniture, she finds her chair is upside down, and her table is broken. What is the size of the angle between the table leg and the back of the chair, marked x?

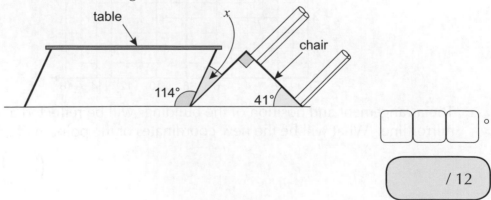

You have **10 minutes** to do this test. Work as quickly and accurately as you can.

1. Momo splits 96 dominoes into 6 piles. How many dominoes are in each pile?

2. Robert measured the width of his father's car.
    Circle the option which is most likely to be the width Robert measured.

    A   19 cm
    B   1.9 m
    C   19 mm
    D   19 m
    E   0.19 km

3. Gustav puts one coin in each of his three piggy banks every day.
    How many coins does he have in total after 62 days? Circle the correct answer.

    A   186   C   246   E   124
    B   126   D   184

4. A factory that operates every day can produce 9 engines a week.
    How many engines can it make in 21 days?

5. Mark thought of a number and wrote it down on squared paper.

| | | 6 | 3 | 1 | 3 | . | 3 | 2 | 5 | | |

Mark tripled his number and wrote it down.
Which number is now in the hundredths column? Circle the correct answer.

    A   6

    B   5

    C   1

    D   7

    E   8

All players in a badminton league play 25 games of badminton.

6. Tanvi won 11 of the games she played. What percentage of games did she win?

                  ☐☐ %

7. Maria's mean score for all her games was 11 points.
How many points did Maria score in total? Circle the correct option.

    A   44

    B   275

    C   154

    D   261

    E   550

8. A large tent is made from 4 fabric panels. One panel is a large square with sides of 5 m. The other panels are rectangles that are 2 m high and 5 m wide.
What is the total area of the fabric used in the tent?

                  ☐☐☐ m²

9. A school won £23 092 to spend on books for their 387 pupils.
    Circle the best estimate for the amount of money they spend on each pupil.

    A £0.60   **C** £59.67   **E** £5966.93

    B £5.97   **D** 596.69

The conversion graph for converting Northern francs into Southern pounds is below.

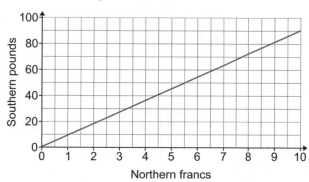

10. Sam wants to convert 60 Southern pounds.
    Use the conversion graph to estimate how many Northern francs he will receive.

    ⬜⬜.⬜⬜

11. Radek has 200 Northern francs. How many Southern pounds could he exchange
    them for? Circle the correct option.

    A 1800 Southern pounds   **D** 900 Southern pounds

    B 220 Southern pounds   **E** 22 Southern pounds

    C 180 Southern pounds

12. Nasrin used 5 litres of paint to cover a wall measuring 15 m². If the paint
    is sold in 2 litre tubs, what area of wall could she paint with 12 tubs?

    ⬜⬜⬜ m²

    / 12

Time for a break! This puzzle is a great way to practise your maths skills.

Buried Treasure

Captain Jack Pigeon is trying to find some pirate treasure buried on an island.

He has a map divided into numbered squares, and a list of instructions left for him by his great-grandfather, Captain Bluebird.

Can you use the instructions to work out in which square the treasure is buried?

57	58	59	60	61	62	63	64
49	50	51	52	53	54	55	56
41	42	43	44	45	46	47	48
33	34	35	36	37	38	39	40
25	26	27	28	29	30	31	32
17	18	19	20	21	22	23	24
9	10	11	12	13	14	15	16
1	2	3	4	5	6	7	8

N ↑

The treasure is __not__ buried...
- under a blue square
- under an even number
- under a prime number
- under a number at the edge of the map
- under a square that is horizontally, vertically or diagonally next to a square number

62

© CGP — not to be photocopied

You have **10 minutes** to do this test. Work as quickly and accurately as you can.

1. Five pupils measured the amount of water their families drank at a meal.
    The values they recorded were: 900 ml, 1.3 litres, 750 ml, 0.62 litres, and 1600 ml.
    If these values are put in order from largest to smallest, which value would be in
    second position? Circle the correct option.

    A   900 ml   C   750 ml   E   1600 ml

    B   1.3 litres   D   0.62 litres

In a survey of 1000 people, 370 people said that they enjoyed swimming.
In the same survey, 260 people said they went swimming regularly.

2. How many people did not say that they enjoyed swimming?

3. What percentage of those asked did not say that they go swimming regularly?

4. $^1/_8$ of the sweets in a packet are strawberry flavour. Oliver buys two packets, each
    containing 32 sweets. How many are strawberry flavour? Circle the correct answer.

    A   12   C   16   E   8

    B   4   D   6

5. A hotel contains 80 rooms. Every bedroom in the hotel has seven electrical
    sockets. In total, fifteen electrical sockets in bedrooms are broken.
    How many working electrical sockets are there in total in all the bedrooms?

A rectangular playing field containing a football pitch has sides of 45 m and 20 m.

6. What is the perimeter of the playing field?

 m

7. A second playing field in the shape of a parallelogram is next to the rectangular playing field. The second playing field has the same length and width as the rectangular playing field. What is the area of the second field?

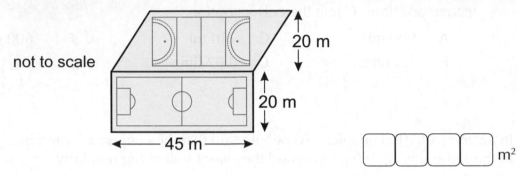

not to scale

20 m

20 m

45 m

 m²

8. A busy telephone call centre receives a call every second. How many calls does the centre receive in two hours?

9. Imogen's cat is 4.8 years old. Use estimation to work out how many days old the cat is. Circle the correct option.

    A   1425 days   **C**   861 days   **E**   2836 days

    B   1753 days   **D**   1297 days

10. Sandra pushes a roundabout in a playground. The roundabout completes 60% of a full turn. How many degrees are left until the roundabout has completed a full turn? Circle the correct answer.

   A   300°

   B   60°

   C   216°

   D   144°

   E   252°

11. Tara thought of a sequence. The first number in her sequence is 41, the second is 49, the third is 56 and the fourth is 62.
   What is the sixth number in Tara's sequence?

12. A bus company calculates the cost of its tickets by charging £1.50, plus 50p per kilometre travelled. This means that the cost of a ticket for a journey of d kilometres is given by the formula: cost = $1.5 + 0.5d$.
   Nina was charged £3.50, how far did she travel? Circle the correct option.

   A   2 km

   B   2.5 km

   C   3 km

   D   3.5 km

   E   4 km

/ 12

© CGP — not to be photocopied

Test 19

You have **10 minutes** to do this test. Work as quickly and accurately as you can.

1. There are seventy football shirts in the laundry room of a football club. Twenty are away shirts, the rest are home shirts. What fraction of the shirts are home shirts? Circle the correct answer.

   A $^1/_7$ C $^4/_7$ E $^6/_7$

   B $^2/_7$ D $^5/_7$

2. A hall contains lots of square tables with sides of 90 cm.
   Noah places four tables together in a straight line.
   How long is the line of tables in metres? Circle the correct answer.

   A 3.6 m   C 0.18 m   E 360 m

   B 1.8 m   D 0.36 m

3. A surveyor measured an electricity pylon as being 415.05 m tall.
   What is this rounded to the nearest 10 metres?

   ☐☐☐.☐ m

4. A normal 6-sided dice has sides of length 3 cm. What is its volume?

   ☐☐☐ cm³

Lunchtime at Down High primary school starts at 12:25 and lasts for 65 minutes.

5. Brian spends six whole lunchtimes working on an art project.
    How long, in minutes, does he spend on his art project at lunchtime?

    ⬚⬚⬚⬚ minutes

6. On a clock in a classroom, the big hand is pointing at IV and the little hand is
    pointing just after X. How long is it until lunchtime?

    ⬚⬚ hours, ⬚⬚ minutes

7. A drink is made by adding water to squash in the ratio 8:1.
    How many litres of the drink can be made with 9 litres of squash?

    ⬚⬚⬚⬚ litres

8. A hockey club plotted a graph of their position in their league against the
    total number of hours the team had trained since the beginning of the season.

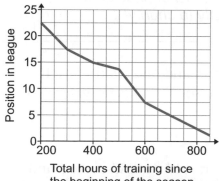

Total hours of training since
the beginning of the season

    The captain told the team that the more the team trains, the worse their position
    becomes. Why is the graph misleading? Circle the correct option.

    A   The line isn't straight.
    B   It looks like the league position is lowest when time spent training is highest.
    C   The graph doesn't show their final position in the league.
    D   The axis showing number of hours training doesn't start at 0.
    E   The axis showing the position in the league starts at 0.

9. Becky thinks of a number, adds 3, then halves the number and subtracts 2.
   Her final number is 21, what number did she think of? Circle the correct option.

   A 12   **C** 43   **E** 41
   B 39   **D** 9

10. A zoo uses two buckets of bananas each day to feed six monkeys.
    How many buckets of bananas will they need each day to feed fifteen monkeys?

    A 4   **C** 6   **E** 8
    B 5   **D** 7

A poster for a charity concert is shown below.

Charity Concert!

Ticket prices

Adults.............................£9

Children..........................£5

*75% of ticket price goes
directly to charity!*

11. Alec bought one adult's ticket and one child's ticket.
    How much of the money he spent on his tickets goes to the charity?

    £

12. The organisers of the concert sold a adult's tickets and c children's tickets.
    The concert raised £75 000 for charity. Which option below shows the equation
    for the total money taken from ticket sales? Circle the correct option.

    A $9a + 5c = 75\ 000$ **D** $9a + 5c = 100\ 000$
    B $5a + 9c = 100\ 000$ **E** $5a + 9c = 75\ 000$
    C $9c + 5a = 50\ 000$

/ 12

Time for a break! This puzzle is a great way to practise your maths skills.

Knights of the Chess Board

King Arthur, Queen Guinevere and Sir Lancelot are comparing the size of their sword collections.

They're a bit shy, so they recorded their results on a chess board that can only be decoded by moving like a knight.

In chess, the knight can only move two squares forward then one space sideways, like this: →

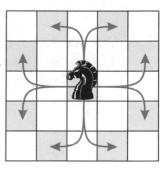

Can you decode the sentence from the chess board so that you can put King Arthur, Queen Guinevere and Sir Lancelot in order of the number of swords they have?

(Hint: start with a name)

fewer	but	has	than
Lancelot	swords	has	Arthur
he	than	Guinevere	more

© CGP — not to be photocopied

You have **10 minutes** to do this test. Work as quickly and accurately as you can.

1. Roger has 189 daffodils. He sells them in bunches of 9.
    He wants to make as many bunches as possible.
    How many bunches can he make? Circle the correct option.

    A 18   **C** 21   **E** 22
    B 16   **D** 11

2. One weekend, Luca runs for 2 hours 14 minutes on Saturday, and then runs for
    3 hours 50 minutes on Sunday. How long does he run for in total on that weekend?

    ☐ hours, ☐☐ minutes

3. A blender uses six apples to make 900 ml of juice.
    How much juice will it make from blending 4 apples?

    ☐☐☐☐ ml

4. Harry gets a box of 24 chocolates. He eats 4 straight away, and then eats ¹/₄ of the
    remaining chocolates the next day. How many chocolates does Harry have left?
    Circle the correct option.

    A 9   **C** 13   **E** 17
    B 11   **D** 15

5. An international phone call costs 15p per minute. Rita makes an international call that lasts 1 hour 40 minutes. How much does Rita's phone call cost?

£  ⬚⬚.⬚⬚

6. Tara and Petr are playing a board game that is played on a coordinate grid. The positions of their counters are shown below.

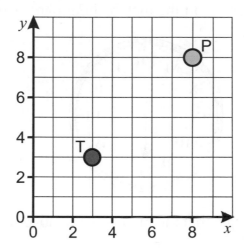

Tara moves her counter two grid squares left and three grid squares up.
Petr moves his counter two grid squares down. How many squares away from Petr's counter is Tara's counter now? Circle the correct option.

A 0	**C** 4	**E** 7
B 3	**D** 5	

A stationery company sells 2 different sizes of sticky notes —
12 cm × 7 cm and 10 cm × 6 cm.

7. What's the difference in area between the two types of sticky note?

⬚⬚⬚ cm²

8. The sticky notes come in packs of 100. Each pack is 0.9 cm thick.
How thick is each sticky note, in millimetres? Circle the correct option.

A 0.9 mm	**C** 900 mm	**E** 0.009 mm
B 90 mm	**D** 0.09 mm	

9. Donna got $^5/_6$ of the questions correct in a maths test.
    There were 48 questions on the test. How many did Donna get correct?

    ☐☐

Rae has a clock, but notices one morning that the hour hand is missing.

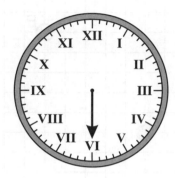

10. What is the size of the angle that the minute hand moves each minute?
    Circle the correct option.

    A 1°   **C** 6°   **E** 12°
    B 5°   **D** 10°

11. Rae works out that on the clock above, the position of the hour hand should be
    75° anticlockwise from the position of the minute hand. What is the time?

    ☐☐ : ☐☐ am

12. Paula has a teapot collection. Each week she sells one teapot, but immediately
    buys three more to replace it. In Week 1, she has two teapots. How many teapots
    does she have in Week n? Circle the correct option.

    A 3(n – 1)   **C** 3n – 1   **E** 2n
    B 2n – 1   **D** 3n

    / 12

You have **10 minutes** to do this test. Work as quickly and accurately as you can.

1. Ricardo saw a car in a showroom on sale for £17 498.95.
   What is the cost of the car rounded to the nearest thousand pounds?
   Circle the correct option.

A	£17 500	C	£17 400	E	£17 499
B	£18 000	D	£17 000		

2. A builder cuts a 7.2 m long plank into eight equally-sized shorter sections.
   How long is each section?

   ⬜.⬜⬜ m

$^1/_2$ of the towels in a shop are blue, $^1/_4$ are green and the rest are purple.

3. What fraction of the towels in the shop are purple? Circle the correct answer.

A	$^1/_3$	C	$^1/_2$	E	$^1/_8$
B	$^1/_4$	D	$^3/_4$		

4. There are eleven green towels in the shop. How many blue towels are there?

   ⬜⬜⬜

© CGP — not to be photocopied   73

5.   Two identical square-based pyramids are glued together so that the bases are joined. This makes an octahedron. How many edges are there on the octahedron?

Seven copies of a book weigh 800 g in total.

6.   A number of copies of the book are in a pile. The pile weighs 3.2 kg. How many copies of the book are in the pile?

7.   Each copy costs £3.95. How much do seven copies cost in total?

£

Some bunting is made from isosceles triangles. The shortest side of each triangle is 20 cm long and is attached to a string, as shown below. There is a 10 cm gap between triangles.

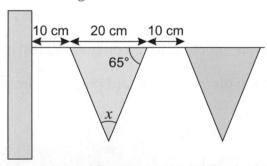

8.   What is the size of the angle marked x?

°

9.   The bunting has to span a 15 m wide street. How many triangles are needed? Circle the correct option.

    A   38   C   50   E   500
    B   750   D   75

10. A boat travels 38 km every hour. How far does the boat travel in 11.5 hours?
    Circle the correct option.

| A | 375 km | C | 437 km | E | 276 km |
| B | 389 km | D | 403 km | | |

11. Greta recorded the length of time she took to get to school
    each day in the table below.

Monday	23 minutes
Tuesday	28 minutes
Wednesday	22 minutes
Thursday	30 minutes
Friday	

The mean length of time Greta took to get to school this week was 26 minutes.
How long did it take her to get to school on Friday? Circle the correct option.

| A | 24 minutes | C | 26 minutes | E | 28 minutes |
| B | 25 minutes | D | 27 minutes | | |

12. Bernard parked his car in an airport's short-stay carpark for fifty minutes.
    The cost in pence of parking for n minutes is given by $60n + 20$.
    How much did Bernard have to pay for his parking?

/ 12

© CGP — not to be photocopied

75

You have **10 minutes** to do this test. Work as quickly and accurately as you can.

1. Andy's family are going to Cornwall.
   Before they set off, his mum's car had travelled this many miles:

    | 0 | 7 | 7 | 3 | 2 | 2 | . | 3 | miles

   They live 421.4 miles from their destination.
   How many miles had the car travelled when they arrived in Cornwall?

   ☐☐☐☐☐☐.☐ miles

2. Tom has a square and two regular pentagons of fabric, each with side length 4 cm.
   He uses them to make the pattern shown below.

   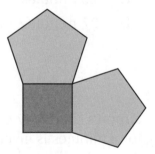

   What is the perimeter of the pattern?

   ☐☐ cm

3. Paul has 312 trading cards which he has sorted into piles of six.
   How many piles of cards does he have? Circle the correct answer.

A	52	**C**	54	**E**	50
B	108	**D**	102		

Skyler made 1000 paper aeroplanes. She made 428 of the aeroplanes from blue paper and the rest from red paper.

4. What fraction of Skyler's paper aeroplanes are made from blue paper?
   Circle the correct answer.

   A $^{428}/_{500}$ **C** $^{114}/_{250}$ **E** $^{132}/_{500}$

   B $^{107}/_{250}$ **D** $^{107}/_{500}$

5. Skyler threw four of her paper aeroplanes. They travelled 10 m, 3 m, 14 m and 15 m. What is the mean distance the aeroplanes travelled?

    m

A school received a delivery of bricks in a shipping container.
The bricks are cuboids with square ends, as shown below.

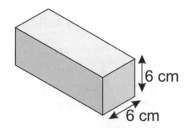

6. Each brick has a volume of 720 cm³. How long is each brick?

    cm

7. The shipping container has a volume of 37 440 000 cm³ and is full of bricks.
   Estimate the number of bricks in the container. Circle the correct answer.

   A 52 000   **C** 5 200   **E** 520

   B 520 000   **D** 5 200 000

8. A recycling lorry has to pick up recycling from 800 homes.
   35% of the homes forgot to put out their recycling boxes.
   How many homes forgot to put out their recycling?

Luke makes 1.8 litres of juice every day.

9. How much juice does he make over 31 days?

 litres

10. How many days will it take Luke to make 162 litres of juice?

 days

11. The percentage of banana in Luke's smoothie changes by the same amount each day. On the first day, Luke's smoothie was 3% banana.
On the second day it was 8% banana and on the third day it was 13%.
On which day will the percentage of banana first be over 30%?

Day ☐☐

12. Sandy is using a coordinate grid to plot how a sail on a windmill moves.

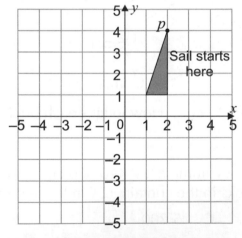

When the sail is rotated by 180° about (0, 0), what are the coordinates of point p?
Circle the correct answer.

A (−2, 4)   **C** (4, −2)   **E** (−4, 2)

B (−2, −4)   **D** (−4, −2)

/ 12

Time for a break! This puzzle is a great way to practise your maths skills.

Crossnumbersearch

All of the numbers below fit into the crossword grid — except one.
Complete the grid. Which number doesn't fit?

36	608	4747	41 803	91 260 517
58	916	5364	68 698	97 160 320
486	1400	9491	99 589	2 204 846 279
547	1693	40 051	57 643 764	7 948 803 567

You have **10 minutes** to do this test. Work as quickly and accurately as you can.

1. Sally divides £36 equally between forty of her friends.
    How many much money does each person receive? Circle the correct option.

    A £1.30   **C** £1.20   **E** £0.90

    B £0.60   **D** £0.40

2. One yard is approximately 0.91 metres. A sweetshop sells giant milk chocolates
    in packets that are one yard long and giant dark chocolates in packets that are
    1 metre long. Approximately how much longer are dark chocolate packets than
    milk chocolate packets? Circle the right answer.

    A 90 cm   **C** 9 cm   **E** 0.9 m

    B 0.9 cm   **D** 9 mm

Irwin asked his class to choose the type of tree they liked best from a list of five.
He plotted his results on a bar graph.

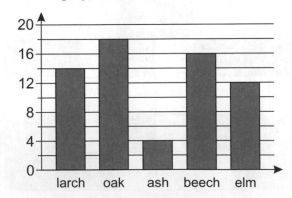

3. How many said they liked the larch best?

4. How many more people chose the most popular type
    of tree than the least popular type of tree?

5. An airline has two sorts of plane. Its jet planes can travel 850 miles in 94 minutes. Its propeller-driven planes fly at half the speed of its jet planes. How far can its propeller-driven planes fly in 188 minutes? Circle the correct answer.

A	3400 miles	**C**	2550 miles	**E**	425 miles
B	850 miles	**D**	950 miles		

An arris rail is a wooden triangular prism used to make fences.
The end faces of an arris rail are right-angled triangles with a surface area of 11 cm².

6. What is the volume of a 100 cm long arris rail?

$$\boxed{}\boxed{}\boxed{}\boxed{}\boxed{}\ \text{cm}^3$$

7. Eight arris rails are arranged as shown.

What is the total area of each end face of the arrangement?

$$\boxed{}\boxed{}\boxed{}\ \text{cm}^2$$

8. Jaromír used 75 eggs to completely fill three large egg boxes. How many eggs can he fit in 60 large egg boxes?

$$\boxed{}\boxed{}\boxed{}\boxed{}$$

9. A new type of freight train is being tested. As part of the test it has to cover
    4197.0 km and travels 113.4 km every hour. Estimate how many hours it takes for
    the train to complete this part of the test. Circle the correct option.

    A   370 hours   **C**   37.0 hours   **E**   3.7 hours

    B   250 hours   **D**   25.0 hours

Pete wants to buy enough brown paint to cover every wall of a new house,
and enough white paint to cover all the ceilings.

10. He estimates that he needs enough brown paint to cover 230 m².
     1 litre of paint can cover 10 m². A shop sells 5 litre tubs of brown paint for £13.
     How much does Pete need to spend on brown paint?

     £ ☐☐ . ☐☐

11. Pete has three identical square rooms. He estimates that he needs to buy enough
     white paint to cover 192 m². What is the length of each side of these rooms?
     Circle the correct answer.

     A   12 m   **C**   16 m   **E**   8 m

     B   20 m   **D**   9 m

12. It takes $n(n + 3)$ minutes to serve a group of n people at a restaurant.
     How long will it take to serve a table of nine people?

     ☐☐☐ minutes

     / 12

You have **10 minutes** to do this test. Work as quickly and accurately as you can.

1. Wendy uses a £5 note to buy two lettuces for 49p each.
    How much change should she receive?

    £

2. Evan paints two faces of a model square-based pyramid red and paints all
    the other faces green. How many faces are green? Circle the correct answer.

A 1	**C** 3	**E** 5
B 2	**D** 4	

Five pupils picked up a leaf each from the playground and measured their lengths.
The lengths they measured were 7.7 cm, 0.05 m, 28 mm, 0.1 m and 49 mm.

3. When ordered from shortest to longest, which value is in fourth position?
    Circle the correct answer.

A 7.7 cm	**C** 28 mm	**E** 49 mm
B 0.05 m	**D** 0.1 m	

4. What is the difference in length between the longest leaf and the shortest one?
    Give your answer in centimetres.

    ⬚.⬚⬚ cm

© CGP — not to be photocopied   83

Mrs Holmes drew a pie chart to show the colour of her 32 pupils' socks.

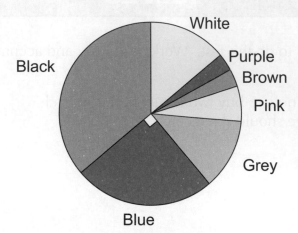

5. What fraction of Mrs Holmes's class wore blue socks? Circle the correct option.

    A $^2/_3$ **C** $^1/_4$ **E** $^1/_5$

    B $^1/_6$ **D** $^1/_3$

6. 16 children wore black or white socks.
    How many wore purple, brown, pink or grey socks?

7. At a rugby match, 95% of the seats are filled, and there are 3300 empty seats.
    How many seats are there in the stadium?

    A 30 300   **C** 66 000   **E** 60 600

    B 20 000   **D** 33 000

8. Erica has to move boxes of stationery from a lorry to a warehouse.
    Each box of stationery weighs 800 g. Erica can carry a maximum of 9 kg at once.
    How many trips from the lorry to the warehouse will it take her to move 35 boxes
    of stationery?

9. A type of rug is 0.8 m wide and 1.2 m long. Two of these rugs are placed side-by-side. What is the combined area of both rugs?

$$\boxed{}.\boxed{}\boxed{}\ \text{m}^2$$

There are 48 people in a school orchestra. $\frac{3}{8}$ play violin, $\frac{1}{6}$ play clarinet and 25% are percussionists. Nobody plays more than one instrument.

10. How many don't play either the violin or the clarinet?
    Circle the correct answer.

    A 28   **C** 26   **E** 12

    B 22   **D** 24

11. Everyone in the orchestra practises at home for 30 minutes each day, except for the percussionists who practise for an hour each day. What is the total amount of time that the members of the orchestra spend practising at home each day?

    $$\boxed{}\boxed{}\ \text{hours,}\ \boxed{}\boxed{}\ \text{minutes}$$

Brian thinks of a sequence.
The first five numbers in his sequence are 5, 12, 20, 29, 39.

12. The twelfth number in Brian's sequence is 137 and the eleventh number is 120. What is the tenth number in Brian's sequence?

    $$\boxed{}\boxed{}\boxed{}$$

    $$\boxed{\text{/ 12}}$$

Time for a break! These puzzles are a great way to practise your maths skills.

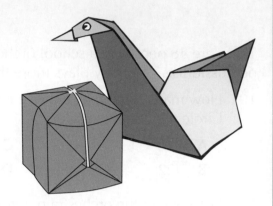

This is a Fold Up!

Ali likes making things out of folded paper.

Her paper is 0.3 mm thick. She folds a large sheet of paper in half six times.

How thick is the wodge of folded paper?

Grab a piece of paper and try for yourself — how many folds can you do?

Ancient Rocks

Four rocks from an ancient civilisation have been found in a woodland.

They all have four numbers carved onto the front.

One of the rocks is partly obscured by a bush.

Which numbers are hidden behind the bush?

Can you think of some other rocks that could be found?

© CGP — not to be photocopied

You have **10 minutes** to do this test. Work as quickly and accurately as you can.

1. The time taken for a scientific process to take place was measured as
    part of an experiment. It was found to take 0.2952 seconds.
    What is this time, rounded to the nearest hundredth of a second?

 s

2. A playing field is in the shape of a regular octagon, as shown.
    How many lines of symmetry does the playing field have?

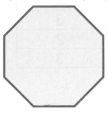

3. A room measures 400 cm by 350 cm.
    What is its area in m²? Circle the correct answer.

    A   140 m²   **C**   14 m²   **E**   140 000 m²

    B   1400 m²   **D**   14 000 m²

4. A 20-sided dice has the numbers 1-20 on its faces.
    What is the ratio of 'sides numbered with a multiple of 6'
    to 'sides numbered with an odd number'? Circle the correct answer.

    A   3:10   **C**   6:10   **E**   10:6

    B   10:3   **D**   3:2

© CGP — not to be photocopied

5. The sequence below shows the distances in metres of some fence posts from the end of a garden. All the fence posts are to be equally spaced out in a line. How far from the end of the garden (in m) will the next two fence posts be?

    $\frac{1}{2}$, $1\frac{1}{4}$, 2, $2\frac{3}{4}$, _____, _____

    Circle the correct answer below.

    A $3\frac{3}{4}$ and $4\frac{1}{2}$ **C** $3\frac{1}{2}$ and $4\frac{1}{2}$ **E** $3\frac{1}{2}$ and $4\frac{1}{4}$

    B $3\frac{1}{4}$ and $3\frac{3}{4}$ **D** $3\frac{1}{4}$ and 4

Thomas spun a 6-sided spinner 20 times. His scores are shown in this table.

Score	Frequency
1	5
2	3
3	4
4	3
5	2
6	3

6. What was his most common score?

7. Thomas wants to show these results in a pie chart.
    What angle will the section showing the least common score make?

    °

8. A firm can make an ornament in 5 hours.
    A new manufacturing process means that this time can be reduced by 30%.
    How long will it take the firm to make an ornament in the future?

    hours   minutes

9. 30 cards need to be split into a number of piles of equal size.
    The number of cards in each pile has to be a prime number.
    What is the largest number of cards that can be in each pile?

Four tiles in the shape of regular 10-sided polygons are arranged into the design shown below.

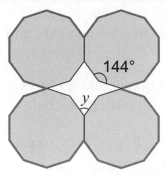

10. How big is angle y?

11. The region between the four tiles has a perimeter of 40 cm.
The perimeter of the whole design is shown in dark blue.
How long is the perimeter of the whole design?

 cm

12. The total amount in pounds (C) charged by an electrician includes two parts:
   - a call-out charge of £30
   - a charge of £15 for each hour

   Which of the formulas below gives the total cost (in pounds) for a job which takes the electrician h hours? Circle the correct option.

   A $C = 15h + 30$

   B $C = 30h + 15$

   C $C = 30h + 15h$

   D $C = (30 + 15)h$

   E $C = 45h + 15$

/ 12

You have **10 minutes** to do this test. Work as quickly and accurately as you can.

1. Oisin has half a pizza to divide equally into 6 pieces.
    What fraction of a whole pizza will each piece be?
    Circle the correct answer.

    A ¹⁄₆   **C** ¹⁄₈   **E** ¹⁄₃
    B ¹⁄₁₂   **D** ¹⁄₄

2. Malcolm orders 278 kg of bricks for his new shed.
    After one day of bricklaying he has used 92 kg of the bricks.
    What is the mass of the remaining bricks?

     kg

3. A bamboo plant is 4 m tall one morning. During the day its height
    increases by 5%. How tall is it at the end of the day?

     m

4. The blade of a craft knife is shown below.

    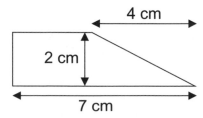

    What is the area of the blade?

    ☐☐ cm²

5.   The two triangles below appear on an architect's scale drawing.
      The two triangles are similar. What is the length d?

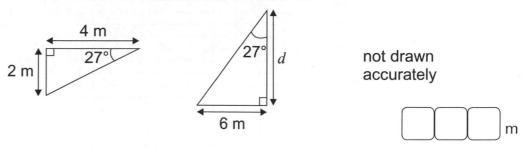

not drawn
accurately

☐☐☐ m

6.   Maci is painting her house. She needs $^1/_2$ of a tin of paint for the living
      room and $^2/_3$ of a tin for the kitchen. How much paint will she use
      altogether? Circle the correct answer.

      A $1^1/_3$ tins   **C** $^5/_6$ tins   **E** $1^1/_6$ tins
      B $1^1/_2$ tins   **D**   2 tins

7.   Ray turns a dial on a safe. He turns it 60° clockwise, then a quarter of a turn
      anticlockwise, then 50° clockwise. What single turn would move the dial from its
      original position to its current position? Circle the correct answer.

      A   20° clockwise   **C**   160° clockwise   **E**   10° anticlockwise
      B   100° clockwise   **D**   10° clockwise

8.   A space probe is travelling at 35 650 kilometres per hour.
      Approximately how many metres does it travel in 1 second?
      Circle the correct answer.

      A   10 m   **C**   1000 m   **E**   100 000 m
      B   100 m   **D**   10 000 m

The depth of water in a bird bath during a day is shown in the following time graph.

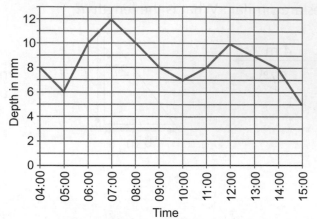

9. What is the difference between the highest depth of water
    in the bird bath and the lowest?

    ⬚⬚ mm

10. During which hour did the depth change the most? Circle the correct answer.

    A Between 04:00 and 05:00

    B Between 05:00 and 06:00

    C Between 06:00 and 07:00

    D Between 07:00 and 08:00

    E Between 08:00 and 09:00

To make a stone column, a stonemason needs to know what the angles in a shape with n sides add up to. He uses this formula to find the sum (S) of the angles: $S = 180(n - 2)$.

11. What do the angles add up to in a shape with 6 sides?

    ⬚⬚⬚⬚ °

12. The cross-section of a stone column is shown below. It is a regular polygon.

    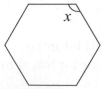

    What is the size of angle x? Circle the correct answer.

    A 108°   **C** 135°   **E** 150°

    B 120°   **D** 140°

    / 12

🕙 **10**

You have **10 minutes** to do this test. Work as quickly and accurately as you can.

1. The price of a new car is reduced by $^1/_5$.
    What is this reduction as a percentage?

     %

2. The plan of a room is shown on the coordinate grid below.
    The hat-stand is translated 2 units south and 1 unit west.

    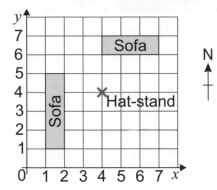

    What are the new coordinates of the hat-stand? Circle the correct answer.

    A (5, 2)   **C** (2, 3)   **E** (2, 5)
    B (3, 2)   **D** (6, 3)

3. A stack of five hundred sheets of paper is 5 cm high.
    What is the thickness of a single sheet of paper? Circle the correct answer.

    A 0.1 cm   **C** 0.001 cm   **E** 0.01 mm
    B 0.1 mm   **D** 0.001 mm

4. Breckin cycles round a track in 8.898 seconds.
    Olivia takes two hundredths of a second longer to cycle round the same track.
    How long did it take Olivia to cycle round the track?

    ☐.☐☐☐ s

© CGP — not to be photocopied   93

5. On a normal dice, what fraction of the sides are numbered with either a multiple of 3 or a multiple of 5? Circle the correct answer.

   A ¹⁄₆   **C** ¹⁄₂   **E** ⁵⁄₆

   B ¹⁄₃   **D** ²⁄₃

6. A firm selling thimbles puts each thimble inside a small container in the shape of a 2 cm cube.
   These containers are then packed into a larger box, as shown below.

   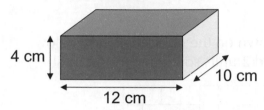

   4 cm
   10 cm
   12 cm

   How many 2 cm containers would fit into this larger box?

7. 2435 raisins are shared out between 8 friends.
   Each friend receives the same number of raisins, but some raisins are left over.
   How many raisins are left over?

The regular polygon below is a scale drawing of a garden.
The point *O* is the centre of the polygon.

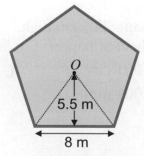

O
5.5 m
8 m

8. What is the perimeter of the garden?

 m

9. What is the area of the garden?

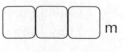 m²

10. Amelie threw a 4-sided dice 6 times. Her scores were 1, 2, 4, 3, 4, 1.
    What was her mean score? Circle the correct option.

    A   1   **C**   2   **E**   2.5

    B   1.25   **D**   2.25

11. The plan for a new flower bed in the shape of a parallelogram is drawn onto a set
    of coordinate axes. Three corners of the parallelogram are shown on the axes.
    Which two points could be used as the fourth corner of the parallelogram?
    Circle the correct answer.

    A   (3, –3) and (–5, –3)

    B   (–3, 3) and (–5, –3)

    C   (3, –3) and (–3, –5)

    D   (–3, –3) and (–5, 3)

    E   (–3, –3) and (–3, –5)

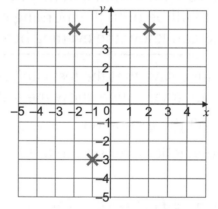

12. Aalia has 6 green sweets and 3 red ones.
    Calum has 8 green sweets and 5 red ones.
    Calum gives 75% of his green sweets and 20% of his red sweets to Aalia.
    What percentage of Aalia's sweets are now red?

                                                          □□ %

                                                           / 12

© CGP — not to be photocopied

Test 28

Puzzles 11

Time for a break! These puzzles are a great way to practise your maths skills.

Testing Times

A teacher tells her class about a surprise test.

> I'll choose one day next week for the test — any day from Monday to Friday.
>
> But it's very important that no one knows exactly when it will be until the morning of the test. No one can know the evening before!

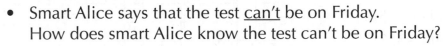

- Smart Alice says that the test <u>can't</u> be on Friday. How does smart Alice know the test can't be on Friday?

- Why can't the test be on Thursday?

- Can the teacher <u>ever</u> set the test?

Stirring Things Up

I have a glass of ink (labelled 1) and a glass of water (labelled 2).

The glasses are the same size and they're filled to the same level.

- I take 100 ml of ink from glass 1 and add it to glass 2, stirring thoroughly.

- I then take 100 ml of 'inky water' from glass 2 and add it to glass 1.

Which is greater...

...the amount of ink in glass 2, or the amount of water in glass 1?

You have **10 minutes** to do this test. Work as quickly and accurately as you can.

1. A firm sells toys for 20% more than they cost to make.
    If it costs the firm £5.50 to make a toy, what is the selling price?

    £

2. Pablo needs to find 2.375 × 1.84, but the decimal point button on his
    calculator is broken. He calculates 2375 × 184 and gets the answer below.

    437000

    What is 2.375 × 1.84? Circle the correct answer.

A	0.0437	**C**	4.37	**E**	437
B	0.437	**D**	43.7		

3. The toy below is an object with 20 faces. Each face is an equilateral triangle.

    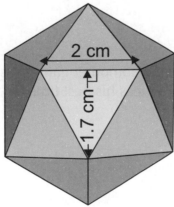

    What is the total area of the object's surfaces?

     cm²

4. I have 16 cards numbered 20-35. What fraction of the cards show multiples of 3?
    Circle the correct answer.

A	$^3/_{16}$	**C**	$^5/_{16}$	**E**	$^1/_3$
B	$^1/_4$	**D**	$^3/_8$		

5. A toy building block is in the form of a cube with sides of length 4 cm.
    Five of these blocks are stacked on top of each other.
    What is the total volume of the stack?

     cm³

A bank asks five of its customers to rate its customer service on a scale of –5 to 5,
where –5 is 'very bad' and 5 is 'very good'. The results are shown below.

Ola	5
Mike	–1
Robin	0
Gemma	5
Sarah	–4

6. What is the difference between Gemma's and Sarah's scores?

7. What is the mean of the scores given by the five customers?

    A   –1   C   0   E   1
    B   –0.2   D   0.2

8. Stuart's best time to complete a computer game was 3 hours and 40 minutes.
    He then plays it again and reduces his best time by 10%.
    What is his new best time?

    [ ] hours, [ ][ ] minutes

9. A cake is left in the kitchen. People arrive in the kitchen one at a time and
    each person takes half of what's left of the cake. So the first person takes
    $\frac{1}{2}$ of the cake, the second person takes $\frac{1}{4}$ of the whole cake, and so on.
    What fraction of the whole cake does the fifth person take?
    Circle the correct answer.

    A $\frac{1}{8}$ C $\frac{1}{32}$ E $\frac{1}{128}$
    B $\frac{1}{16}$ D $\frac{1}{64}$

10. 440 marbles are to be shared out between Andy and Beatrice.
    Beatrice will receive 4 times as many marbles as Andy.
    How many marbles will Andy receive?

11. The graph below was used to show the effect of a new roundabout
    at a busy road junction.

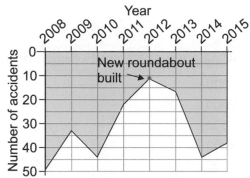

A politician claimed that the graph proves the roundabout reduced the number
of accidents. Why is the graph misleading? Circle the correct answer.

A   The vertical scale doesn't include 0.

B   The years should be on the vertical scale.

C   The numbers on the vertical scale aren't evenly spaced out.

D   Bigger numbers appear lower down on the vertical scale.

E   The vertical scale should be labelled in fives.

12. An energy company uses a formula to find the cost in pounds (C) it should
    charge a customer who has used n units of electricity.
    A customer who has used 200 units of electricity is charged £25.
    Circle the formula below that could link C and n.

A $C = \frac{1}{100}n + 23$

B $C = \frac{1}{10}n + 18$

C $C = 30 + \frac{1}{100}n$

D $C = 100n + 23$

E $C = 10n + 15$

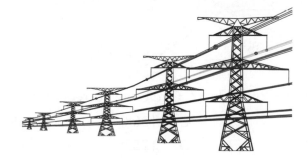

/ 12

© CGP — not to be photocopied

Test 29

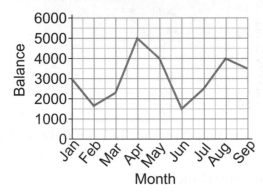
You have **10 minutes** to do this test. Work as quickly and accurately as you can.

1. A set of 40 children's books takes up 30 cm of space on a bookshelf.
    How wide is each book?

    [ ][ ].[ ][ ] cm

This graph shows Adi's bank balance at the start of each month over a 9-month period.

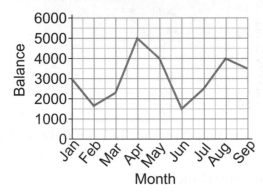

2. If Adi's balance is below £2000 at the start of any month, then he has to pay a fee.
    How many times did he have to pay this fee during this period?

    [ ]

3. What is the difference between the highest balance and the lowest?

    £ [ ][ ][ ][ ]

4. The beams in a house are arranged to form isosceles triangles, as shown below.

    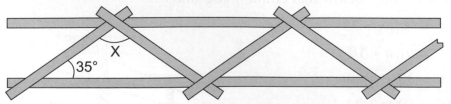

    What is the size of angle X? Circle the correct answer.

    A   35°   **C**   120°   **E**   135°
    B   110°   **D**   125°

© CGP — not to be photocopied

5. A family is buying food for a picnic. A price list for various items is shown below.

Loaf of bread	£1.20
Packet of cheese	£1.10
Jar of pickle	50p

What will it cost to buy 1 loaf of bread, 2 packets of cheese and a jar of pickle?

£

6. This spinner shows the numbers 1-12.

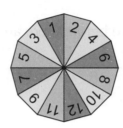

What fraction of the sections show a factor of 12? Circle the correct answer.

A $\frac{1}{6}$ **C** $\frac{1}{3}$ **E** $\frac{1}{2}$

B $\frac{1}{4}$ **D** $\frac{5}{12}$

Sean is running laps of a rectangular football pitch.
The pitch is 75 m long and 45 m wide.

7. How far has he run after 3 laps?

◻◻◻◻ m

8. Sean always runs complete laps of the pitch.
Today he wants to stop as soon as possible, but still run at least 10 km.
How many laps in total does Sean need to run? Circle the correct answer.

A 4   **C** 40   **E** 42

B 5   **D** 41

9. I have 21 black sheep and 35 white sheep.
    I want to divide these sheep up into groups of equal size,
    but the sheep in each group must all be the same colour.
    What is the largest number of sheep that can be in each group?

The number of cars in a car park n minutes after it opens is $3n + 4$.

10. How many cars will there be in the car park 20 minutes after it opens?

11. How many minutes does it take before there are more than 80 cars in the car park?
    Circle the correct answer.

A	24	**C**	26	**E**	28
B	25	**D**	27		

12. The bathroom tile below has a design consisting of 4 identical white triangles.

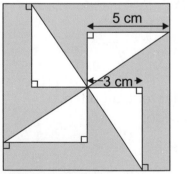

not to scale

What is the area of the blue part of the tile? Circle the correct answer.

A	10 cm²	**C**	34 cm²	**E**	70 cm²
B	30 cm²	**D**	40 cm²		

/ 12

Test 30   102   © CGP — not to be photocopied

You have **10 minutes** to do this test. Work as quickly and accurately as you can.

1. A group of pupils were asked what they drank for breakfast one morning.
    Their results were displayed in a pie chart.

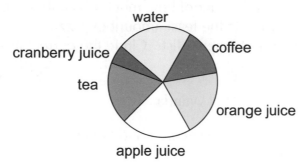

    Which drink was the least popular? Circle the correct option.

    A Tea   **C** Cranberry juice   **E** Apple juice
    B Orange juice   **D** Coffee

A type of dahlia flower always has eight petals.
There are 80 of these dahlias growing on a roundabout.
All the dahlias on the roundabout are either purple or white.

2. What is the total number of dahlia petals on the roundabout?

3. The ratio of purple dahlias to white dahlias on the roundabout is 3:7.
    How many purple dahlias are there?

4. 20% of the dahlias on the roundabout were destroyed during some roadworks.
    How many dahlias are left on the roundabout?

At a picnic, Matthew records in a table how much of a pizza everyone has eaten.

Person	Amount of pizza eaten
Sam	$\frac{1}{2}$
Tahir	$\frac{7}{8}$
Cate	$\frac{4}{5}$
Wanda	$1\frac{1}{3}$
Hayley	$\frac{1}{3}$

5. He then arranges the names in order of how much pizza they ate, starting with the person who ate the least amount of pizza. What is the fourth name on Matthew's list? Circle the correct answer.

A Sam   **C** Cate   **E** Hayley

B Tahir   **D** Wanda

6. What is the difference between the smallest and largest amount of pizza eaten? Circle the correct answer.

A $\frac{4}{5}$ **C** $\frac{7}{8}$ **E** $\frac{5}{6}$

B 1   **D** $\frac{23}{24}$

7. Nathaniel is printing a 63-page document. The printer he's using prints the same number of pages each minute. After 8 minutes the printer had printed 24 pages. How many minutes in total will it take to print the whole document?

8. A card game starts by sharing out 42 cards equally among the players. The number of cards each player receives must be a prime number. What is the minimum possible number of players? Circle the correct answer.

A 2   **C** 6   **E** 21

B 3   **D** 14

9. A shop sells a lunchtime meal deal for a set price.
Philip bought three meal deals for £9.75.
How much change will he receive if he pays for 5 meal deals using a £20 note?

£

A robot is programmed to walk around a triangular route in three stages.
Stage One is 5 m long, Stage Two is 3 m long and Stage Three is 4 metres long.
The angle between Stage One and Stage Two is 53°.
The angle between Stage Two and Stage Three is 90°.

10. What is the angle between Stage One and Stage Three?

 °

11. The robot's battery contains 100 units of energy.
The robot uses up 1 unit of energy for every metre it travels.
How many whole laps of the triangular route can it complete?

12. The drawing below shows one of Farmer Ben's fields.
1 cm on the diagram shows a distance of 10 m on the ground.

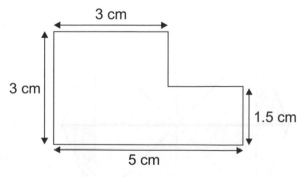

What is the area of the real field? Circle the correct answer.

    A   400 m²   **C**   1200 m²   **E**   2000 m²

    B   1000 m²   **D**   1600 m²

/ 12

Time for a break! These puzzles are a great way to practise your maths skills.

Ridiculous Receipts

Lorna's local shop has a broken printer —
all the numbers on her receipt printed out
with the wrong symbols.

The shopkeeper told her that each symbol
represents a different number.

She paid for her shopping with a £10 note
and received £3.85 in change.

How much did the eggs cost?

```
    SUPERSHOP LTD
eggs        £♥.☆●
flour       £☆.●♉
butter      £♉.●●
sugar       £☆.✦●
_____
TOTAL:      £➤.☆●
```

Seeing Shapes

How many triangles can you count in this picture?
The triangles can be any shape, any size and any colour.

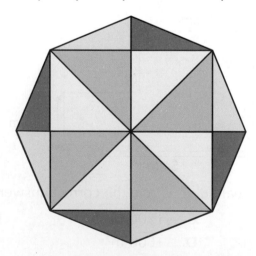

Now count all the quadrilaterals — there might be more than you think.

© CGP — not to be photocopied

MWXPDE1